IN MEMORY OF

DONALD FRIZELL HYDE

WILDE

AND THE NINETIES

AN ESSAY

AND AN EXHIBITION

RICHARD ELLMANN

E. D. H. JOHNSON

ALFRED L. BUSH

EDITED BY CHARLES RYSKAMP

PRINCETON, NEW JERSEY
PRINCETON UNIVERSITY LIBRARY
MCMLXVI

INTRODUCTION

THIS small book is the memorial of a celebration and of sorrow. It came into being because of a remarkable exhibition in the Princeton University Library, and because of the death of Donald Hyde on 5 February 1966, ten days before the exhibition opened.

About a year ago several members of the Department of English suggested that we exhibit our collections in the University Library of English literature and related arts of the 1890's. Princeton's holdings of this period are very good, especially in poetry and periodical literature. But our collection of Oscar Wilde, whose work, as Professor Johnson writes, 'epitomizes the spirit of that age,' is not in any way of equivalent excellence. We therefore naturally turned to two neighbors in order that we might make the exhibition one of distinction throughout. We thought first of all of the outstanding collection of Oscar Wilde formed by Mr. and Mrs. Donald F. Hyde of Somerville, and then of a number of notable items in the library of Mr. Robert H. Taylor of Princeton. The Hydes and Mr. Taylor enthusiastically and generously supported our plans from the beginning. As a consequence the exhibition was unusually fine in almost every aspect of this rich period in English art and letters, although we still found some surprising gaps in the University collections, particularly in certain phases of the Celtic Revival, in the naturalistic novels, in the printing of a few of the private presses of the time, and in the writings more closely tied to contemporary French literary movements. Even these weaknesses, however, may scarcely have been noticed, since important and rare manuscripts and books illustrate these facets of the Nineties as well as all the others.

From the outset we were not only determined to make the exhibition as comprehensive as the gallery would permit, and to use every available resource at hand; but we also wanted to involve the community in such a special show more fully than has usually been the case in the past. The University Library, the Department of English, and McCarter Theatre therefore worked together to make this exhibition part of the life of the University and the town during the winter and spring of 1966. The exhibition itself was largely put together by Mr. Alfred L. Bush, Associate Curator of Manuscripts in the Library. His description should help to make known these three collections to scholars who could not see the exhibition. Professor E. D. H. Johnson of the University's Department of English established the focus of the exhibition and wrote the brochure, reprinted here, which served as its introduction. The winter-spring season of the professional repertory company of the University Theatre was planned around Wilde and the drama of the Nineties, under the rubric, 'The Masks of Love.' The series of plays opened with Wilde's *Lady Windermere's Fan* on 18 February. Four days later, on Washington's birthday, Professor Richard Ellmann of Northwestern University gave the lecture, here printed, which was in effect the formal opening of the exhibition. Professor Ellmann is well known for his books on Irish writers of this period and later—Yeats and Joyce—and he is now engaged in a full-length study of Oscar Wilde.

In introducing Professor Ellmann, Dr. William S. Dix, Librarian of the University, spoke also of our great loss at this time. He said then:

It is with sorrow and something approaching disbelief that many of us here realize that Donald Hyde died two weeks ago. Intensely interested in this exhibition, he and Mrs. Hyde had planned to be here tonight. He had been for many years a member of the Council of the Friends of the Princeton University Library and was a member of the Library's Advisory Council. The great library at Four Oaks Farm which the Hydes built together has attracted a steady stream of scholars, who came seeking rare books and manuscripts and found as well beauty and gaiety. A scholar-collector who applied his discriminating taste to subjects as diverse as Samuel Johnson, Oscar Wilde, and early Japanese manuscripts, Donald Hyde led with enthusiasm and imagination dozens of organizations and adventures in the world of books, a world which can hardly be quite the same again without him.

CHARLES RYSKAMP

THE CRITIC AS ARTIST
AS WILDE

The exhibition here stands as one of many memorials to Donald Hyde. He and Mary Hyde gathered their collections with scholars' care, and shared them with a generosity that ennobled the word 'private.' The distinguished fulfilment of Mr. Hyde's own talents in several directions never hampered his attentiveness to other people's needs. Above all he imparted a sense of the possible variety as well as the intensity of intellectual pursuit, and his early death, while it reminds us of how much he would have done, defines also how very much he did.

Donald Hyde would never have tolerated our being solemn about Oscar Wilde, and it is appropriate that on Washington's birthday we should consider the author of 'The Decay of Lying.' Wilde is the one writer of the Nineties whom everyone still reads, or more precisely, has read. The mixture of frivolity and pathos in his career continues to arrest us. I want to explore that career a little in his own terms of 'The Critic as Artist.'

In 1914 Henry James could complain that there was not enough criticism about to give novelists their bearings, while T. S. Eliot and Saul Bellow have recently regretted, for different reasons and in different tones of voice, that there is now too much. The obtrusive place of the critic today can be related to a methodological emphasis which is conspicuous in other disciplines as well. But Wilde was one of the first to see that the exaltation of the artist required a concomitant exaltation of the critic. If art was to have a special train, the critic must keep some seats reserved on it.

Wilde reached this conclusion by way of two others. The first is that criticism plays a vital role in the creative process. If this sounds like T. S. Eliot admonishing Matthew Arnold, Wilde had expressed it, also as an admonition to Arnold, almost thirty

1

years before. The second is that criticism is an independent branch of literature with its own procedures. 'I am always amused,' says Wilde, 'by the silly vanity of those writers and artists of our day who seem to imagine that the primary function of the critic is to chatter about their second-rate work.' And he complains that 'The poor reviewers are apparently reduced to be the reporters of the police-court of literature, the chroniclers of the doings of the habitual criminals of art.' In protesting the independence of criticism Wilde sounds like an ancestral Northrop Frye. These portentous comparisons do indeed claim virtue by association, and such claims may be broadened. André Gide found Nietzsche less exciting because he had read Wilde, and Thomas Mann in one of his last essays remarks with some chagrin on how many of Nietzsche's aphorisms might have been expressed by Wilde, and how many of Wilde's by Nietzsche. What I think can be urged for Wilde then, is that for his own reasons and in his own way he laid the basis for many critical positions which are still debated in much the same terms, and which we like to attribute to more ponderous names.

When Wilde formulated his theories the public was more hostile to criticism than it is now, and Wilde was flaunting his iconoclasm, his contempt for the unconsidered and so uncritical pieties of his age. This in fact was his mode: Not to speak for the Victorians, or for the prematurely old writers who dithered that they were the end of an era, as if they must expire with the 1800's. Wilde proposed to speak for the young, with even excessive eagerness. His own age was always a little embarrassing for him, because he had already completed a degree at Trinity College, Dublin when he went up to Oxford. He was not above a little deception on this score. In 1877, when he was twenty-three, he sent a poem to Gladstone with a letter saying, 'I am little more than a boy.' And in a poem written that year he spoke of his 'boyish passion' and described himself as 'one who scarce has seen some twenty summers.' This line, in turn, he repeated in his poem 'The Sphinx,' finished when he was forty. Even in court he injudiciously testified he was two years younger than he was, so that he sounds a little like Falstaff shouting to Bardolph during the robbery, 'They hate us youth.' Wilde's mode was calculated juvenescence, and the characters in his books are always being warned by shrewder characters of the danger of listening to people older than themselves. To help reduce that danger, Wilde's characters are invariably parentless. The closest kin allowed is an aunt.

Like Stendhal, Wilde thought of himself as a voice of the age to be, rather than of the one that was fading. Yet like anyone else writing criticism in the later nineteenth century, he had to come to terms with the age that had been, and especially with everybody's parent Matthew Arnold. Wilde sought Arnold's approbation for his first book, *Poems*, in 1881, which he sent with a letter stressing their shared Oxonian connections. These extended, though he wisely did not enforce the claim, to their both having won the Newdigate. Actually their prize-winning poems offer a contrast of manners, Arnold's being just as determined to appear older as Wilde's younger than his years. Arnold replied politely.

But by 1881 Arnold was genuinely old, and seven years later, in 1888, he was dead. Wilde's only book of criticism, *Intentions*, was written during the three years following Arnold's death and published in 1891, as if to take over that critical burden and express what Arnold had failed to say. Yeats thought the book 'wonderful' and Walter Pater handsomely praised it for carrying on, 'more perhaps than any other writer, the brilliant critical work of Matthew Arnold.' Pater's encomium is a reminder, however, not to ignore *him*. There are not two but three critical phases in the late nineteenth century, with Pater transitional between Arnold and Wilde.

In 1864, lecturing from the Oxford Chair of Poetry on 'The Function of Criticism at the Present Time,' Arnold declared—to everyone's lasting memory—that the 'aim of criticism is to see the object as in itself it really is.' This statement went with his demand for 'disinterested curiosity' as the mark of the critic; its inadvertent effect was to put the critic on his knees before the work he was discussing. Not everyone enjoyed this position. Nine years later Walter Pater wrote his preface to *Studies in the History of the Renaissance*. Pretending to agree with Arnold's definition of the aim of criticism, he quoted it, then added, 'the first step towards seeing one's object as it really is, is to know one's impression as it really is, to discriminate it, to realize it distinctly.' But Pater's corollary subtly altered the original proposition; it shifted the center of attention from the rock of the object to the winds of the perceiver's sensations. It made the critic's own work more important as well as more subjective. If observation is still the word, the critic looks within himself as often as out upon the object.

Wilde had been Pater's student, and in *Intentions* eighteen years later he tweaks Arnold's nose with the essay which in its first published form was entitled, 'The True Function and Value of Criticism: with Some Remarks on the Importance of Doing Nothing.' Here Wilde rounded upon Arnold by asserting that the aim of criticism is to see the object as it really is not. This aim might seem to justify the rhapsodical critic of Ruskin and Pater, and Wilde uses them as examples; his contention goes beyond their practice, however; he wishes to free critics from subordination, to grant them a larger share in the production of literature. While he does not forbid them to explain a book, they might prefer, he said, to deepen a book's mystery. (This purpose is amusing but out of date now; who could deepen the mystery of *Finnegans Wake?*) At any rate, their context would be different from that of the creative artist. For just as the artist claimed independence of received experience (Picasso tells us that art is 'what nature is not'), so the critic claimed independence of received books. 'The highest criticism,' according to Wilde, 'is the record of one's own soul.' More closely he explained that the critic must have all literature in his mind and see particular works in that perspective rather than in isolation. Thus he, and we as well, 'shall be able to realize, not merely our own lives, but the collective spirit of the race, and so to make ourselves absolutely modern, in the true meaning of the word modernity. For he to whom the present is the only thing that is present, knows nothing of the age in which he lives. To realize the nineteenth century, one must realize every century that has preceded it and that has contributed to its making.' Through knowledge the critic might become more creative than the creative artist, a paradox which has been expressed with more solemnity by Norman Podhoretz about literature of the present day.

Wilde reached these formulations of his aesthetic ideas late in his short life. They were latent, however, in his earliest known essay, 'The Rise of Historical Criticism,' which he wrote as a university exercise. While praising historians for their scrupulousness, Wilde finds the core of history to be the wish not merely to paint a picture, but to investigate laws and tendencies. He celebrates those historians who impose dominion upon fact instead of surrendering to it. Later he was to say much more boldly, 'The one duty we owe to history is to rewrite it.' It is part of his larger conception that the one duty (or better, whim) we owe nature, reality, or the world, is to reconstruct it.

When Wilde turned to literary as distinguished from historical criticism, he at first was content to follow Pater. Wilde was won by Pater's espousal of gemlike flames and of high temperatures both in words and in life. Next to him Arnold sounded chilly, never so Victorian as when he was cogently criticizing Victorianism. That word 'impression,' with which Pater sought to unlock everything, became a favorite word in both Wilde and later in Arthur Symons, and was only arrested by Yeats in the late 1890's because he could not bear so much impermanence and insisted on a metaphysical basis—the Anima Mundi—for transitory moods. Like the word 'absurd' today, though without a systematic philosophy behind it, the word 'impression' agitated against pat assumptions and preconceptions.

Pater's vocabulary shapes the initial poem of Wilde's book of verse, published when he was 25. This poem, 'Hélas!', encapsulates much of Wilde's temperament, but with Pater's coloring:

5

Hélas!

To drift with every passion till my soul
Is a stringed lute on which all winds can play,
Is it for this that I have given away
Mine ancient wisdom, and austere control?
Methinks my life is a twice-written scroll
Scrawled over on some boyish holiday
With idle songs for pipe and virelay
Which do but mar the secret of the whole.
Surely there was a time I might have trod
The sunlit heights, and from life's dissonance
Struck one clear chord to reach the ears of God:
Is that time dead? lo! with a little rod
I did but touch the honey of romance—
And must I lose a soul's inheritance?

To call the poem 'Hélas!', to sigh in a foreign language, alerts us that the confession to follow will luxuriate in its penitence. The Biblical archaisms which occur later offer compunction suitably perfumed. 'To drift' may well put us off as weak; on the other hand, 'to drift with every passion' is not so bad. As its image of passivity the poem offers 'a stringed lute on which all winds can play.' For the romantics the Aeolian harp was a favorable image because it harmonized man and nature. Here the winds are winds of temptation, rather than gusts of Lake Country air. The rhetorical question which begins, 'Is it for this?' sounds reproachful enough, yet the phrases 'ancient wisdom' and 'austere control'—self-congratulatory since Wilde never had either—are so vague as to constitute a stately but equally unenergetic alternative to drifting.

The word 'drift' comes down from Oxford in the 1870's. It occupies a prominent position in Pater's *Studies in the History of the Renaissance,* and specifically in the notorious conclusion to that book. This 'Conclusion' was included in the edition of 1873, but omitted in 1877, when Wilde was Pater's student, on the ground that it 'might possibly mislead' the young, who ac-

6

cordingly thronged to be misled by the first edition. It was the boldest thing Pater ever wrote; he drew upon the scientific work of his day to deny the integrity of objects. Physical life is now recognized, he says, to be a concurrence of forces rather than a group of things; the mind has no fixities either. He hits upon a metaphor of liquidity such as William James and Bergson were to adopt a little later in characterizing consciousness as a river or stream; Pater says more balefully that consciousness is a whirl-pool, an image which later both Yeats and Pound relished. In our physical life, Pater grants, we sometimes feel momentarily at rest; in our consciousness, however, altering the whirlpool image, he finds 'nothing but the race of the mid-stream, a drift of momentary acts of sight and passion and thought.' To drift is not so wanton, then, as inevitable. To guide our drifting we should rely not on sights or thoughts, in Pater's view, but on 'great passions.' 'Only be sure it is passion,' he puts in as a caveat. He urges his readers to recognize that 'not the fruit of experi-ence, but experience itself, is the goal.' 'Our one hope lies in get-ting as many pulsations as possible into the given time.' This attempt to render experience in terms of quantitatively meas-urable pulsations sounds a little like *Principles of Literary Criti-cism,* but Pater's tone is not like Richards'; he plays on the flute for the young to follow him.

When Pater at last decided to reprint this 'Conclusion' (in 1888), he toned it down a little. In *Marius the Epicurean* (1885), also later, the word 'drift' is again prominent, but this time is pejorative instead of merely descriptive. To suit his later and more decorous manner Pater, in reviewing *Dorian Gray,* complained of the book's 'dainty Epicurean theory' because, he said, 'A true Epicureanism aims at a complete though harmo-nious development of man's entire organism. To lose the moral sense therefore, for instance, the sense of sin and righteousness, . . . is to lose, or lower, organisation, to become less complex, to pass from a higher to a lower degree of development.' The letting-go, as well as the drawing-back, of Pater are both evident in Wilde. His work celebrates both impulses, balancing or dis-

7

porting with them. In a letter of March 1877, written four years before 'Hélas!', he informs an Oxford friend,

> I have got rather keen on Masonry lately and believe in it awfully—in fact would be awfully sorry to have to give it up in case I secede from the Protestant Heresy. I now breakfast with Father Parkinson, go to St Aloysius, talk sentimental religion to Dunlop and altogether am caught in the fowler's snare, in the wiles of the Scarlet Woman —I may go over in the vac. I have dreams of a visit to Newman, of the holy sacrament in a new Church, and of a quiet and peace afterwards in my soul. I need not say, though, that I shift with every breath of thought and am weaker and more self-deceiving than ever.
>
> If I *could hope* that the Church would wake in me some earnestness and purity I would go over *as a luxury*, if for no better reasons. But I can hardly hope it would, and to go over to Rome would be to sacrifice and give up my two great gods 'Money and Ambition.'

In this letter Wilde testifies playfully to the same yearning to be earnest that he shows in 'Hélas!' and then mocks in his later comedy. He is half-converted to Catholicism, half to Masonry— that these two groups cannot bear each other does not prevent their being equally attractive to him; they have parity as new areas of sensation, to be enjoyed wilfully and passingly. If, as Wilde announced later, 'the best way to resist temptation is to yield to it,' the reason is that having done so, one may pass on to the next and the next, and in this concourse one may keep a residual freedom by not lingering with any single temptation long.

During the four years between writing this letter and writing 'Hélas!', Wilde had put aside both Catholicism and Masonry. In his sonnet he has in mind chiefly his formal education as contrasted with his romantic self-indulgence. A classicist by training, Wilde considered Hellenism to be the more basic side of his nature, overlaid, but only as a palimpsest conceals the original, by a more modern mode. He berates himself, gently. His new life is made up of 'idle songs for pipe and virelay,' a self-accusation which only concedes frivolity, not depravity. Moreover, it is artistic frivolity, a further mitigation. Wilde remembered Pater's comment in the same 'Conclusion' that 'the wisest' instead of living spend their lives in 'art and song.' If it is wrong to drift, and Wilde hedges a little, then it is less wrong to drift gracefully. A 'boyish holiday' is also not the most offensive way to spend one's time, especially if one likes boys.

The sestet of the poem restates the issue, with new dashes of metaphor. The poet then asks histrionically, 'Is that time dead?' He won't say for sure, but again he sweetens his offense: he has but touched with a little rod the honey of romance. The last question is not so much despairing as hopeful. Wilde felt he was superior to both classical and romantic modes, because he could manipulate both: he said in his essay on the English renaissance that this variability was the strength of the new movement in letters to which he belonged. He thought he had physiological as well as artistic support for his method, because 'the desire of any very intensified emotion [is] to be relieved by some emotion that is its opposite.' He shifts therefore from foot to foot in other poems besides 'Hélas!'. 'The Sphinx' begins with a fascinated invocation of the sphinx and ends with a strident rejection of her. He summarizes his state or rather his flow of mind in a letter:

> Sometime you will find, even as I have found, that there is no such thing as a romantic experience; there are romantic memories, and there is the desire of romance— that is all. Our most fiery moments of ecstasy are merely shadows of what somewhere else we have felt, or of what we long some day to feel. So at least it seems to me. And, strangely enough, what comes of all this is a curious mixture of ardour and of indifference. I myself would sacrifice everything for a new experience, and I know there is

9

no such thing as a new experience at all. I think I would more readily die for what I do not believe in than for what I hold to be true. I would go to the stake for a sensation and be a sceptic to the last! Only one thing remains infinitely fascinating to me, the mystery of moods. To be master of these moods is exquisite, to be mastered by them more exquisite still. Sometimes I think that the artistic life is a long and lovely suicide, and am not sorry that it is so.

Life then is a willed deliquescence, or more exactly, a progressive surrender of the self to all the temptations appropriate to it.

What Wilde needed was not to avoid the precious occasions of evil in 'Hélas!' but to approach more enterprising ones. Yet after his *Poems* appeared in 1881 he was at check for almost six years. He kept busy; he went on a lecture tour for a whole year to America; he returned to England and went lecturing on; he tried unsuccessfully for a post as school inspector such as Matthew Arnold had; erratically still, he married in 1884 and took up 'husbanding,' begetting two children born in 1885 and 1886. Then in 1887 Wilde began the publications by which he is known. He wrote a volume of stories, and one of fairy tales, then one of criticism, then five plays, besides editing from 1887 to 1889 a magazine, *Woman's World*—a patrician equivalent of the A & P *Woman's Day*. It would seem that something roused him from the pseudo-consolidation of marriage and lectures, which were dilettantism for him, to genuine consolidation which seemed dilettantism to others.

This something appears in the original version of *The Picture of Dorian Gray*, published in *Lippincott's Magazine*. Wilde emphasizes more there than in the final version the murder of the painter Basil Hallward by Dorian; it is the turning-point in Dorian's experience, a plunge from insinuations of criminal tendency to crime itself. The murder at once protects the secret of his double life and vents his revulsion against the man who wants him innocent still. In *Lippincott's* Wilde specifies: 'It was on the 7th of November, the eve of his own thirty-second birthday, as he often remembered afterwards. . . .' Then when the novel was published as a book, Wilde altered this date: 'It was on the ninth of November, the eve of his own thirty-eighth birthday, as he often remembered afterwards.'

Altering Dorian's age would be gratuitous if Wilde had not attached significance to his own thirty-second birthday in 1886. The passage must have been autobiographical, and such a conjecture receives support from Robert Ross, who boasted that it was he, at the age of 17, who in the year 1886 first seduced Wilde to homosexual practices. Wilde evidently considered this sudden alteration of his life a pivotal matter, to be recast as Dorian's murder of Hallward. He himself moved from pasteboard marriage to the expression of long latent proclivities, at some remove from the 'ancient wisdom' and 'austere control' to which he had earlier laid claim as his basic nature. Respectability, always an enemy, was destroyed in his own house. The first work which came out of the new Wilde was, appropriately, 'Lord Arthur Savile's Crime,' in which murder is comically enacted and successfully concealed.

From late in the year 1886 then, Wilde was able to think of himself, if he wanted to, as criminal. Up to that time he could always consider himself an innocent misunderstood; now he lived in such a way as to confirm suspicions. Instead of challenging Victorian society only by words, he acted in such a way as to create scandal. Indiscreet by nature, he was indiscreet also by conviction, and he waged his war somewhat openly. He sensed that his new life was a source of literary effect. As he wrote later of Thomas Wainewright: 'His crimes seem to have had an important effect upon his art. They gave a strong personality to his style, a quality that his early work certainly lacked.' He returned to this idea: 'One can fancy an intense personality being created out of sin,' and in 'The Soul of Man Under Socialism,' he thought that 'Crime . . . under certain conditions, may be said to have created individualism.' In 'The Portrait of Mr. W. H.'

(1889), he made Shakespeare's sonnets depend upon a similarly forbidden love affair, with the boy actor Willie Hughes. Thomas Mann's Tonio Kröger speaks of a banker who discovers his literary talent by committing a serious crime for which he is put in prison. The artist-criminal is implicit in romantic and symbolistic theories of art, but Wilde anticipates the explicitness of both Mann and Gide on this subject. He might have discounted the sinfulness of his conduct, and applied to himself his own epigram: 'Wickedness is a myth invented by good people to account for the curious attractiveness of others.' But he was quite content to think of himself as sinful.

He now succeeded in relating his new discoveries about himself to aesthetic theory. His only formal book of criticism, *Intentions*, has the same secret spring as his later plays and stories. Ostensibly he generally says that the spheres of art and of ethics are absolutely distinct and separate. But occasionally, overtly or covertly, he states that for the artist crime does pay, by instilling itself in his content and affecting his form. Each of the four essays that make up *Intentions* is to some degree subversive, as if to demonstrate that the intentions of the artist are not strictly honorable. The first and the last, 'The Decay of Lying' and 'The Truth of Masks,' celebrate art for rejecting truths, faces, and all that paraphernalia in favor of lies and masks. Wilde doesn't do this in the romantic way of extolling the imagination, for while he uses that word he is a little chary of it; the imagination is itself too natural, too involuntary, for his view of art. He prefers lying because it sounds more wilful, because it is no outpouring of the self, but a conscious effort to mislead. 'All fine imaginative work,' Wilde affirms, 'is self-conscious and deliberate. . . . A great poet sings because he chooses to sing.' On the other hand, 'if one tells the truth, one is sure, sooner or later, to be found out!' 'All bad poetry springs from genuine feeling.' Wilde celebrates art not in the name of Ariel, as the romantics would, but in the name of Ananias.

He finds art to have two basic energies, both of them subversive. One asserts its magnificent isolation from experience, its unreality, its sterility. He would concur with Nabokov that art is a kind of trick played on nature, an *illicit* creation by man. 'All art is entirely useless,' Wilde declares. 'Art never expresses anything but itself.' 'Nothing that actually occurs is of the smallest importance.' Form determines content, not content form, a point which Auden also sometimes affirms and which is often assumed by symbolists. With this theory Wilde turns Taine upon his head; the age does not determine what its art should be, rather it is art which gives the age its character. So far from responding to questions posed by the epoch, art offers answers before questions have been asked. 'It is the ages that are her symbols.' Life, straggling after art, seizes upon forms in art to express itself, so that life imitates art rather than art life. '. . . This unfortunate aphorism about Art holding the mirror up to Nature, is,' according to Wilde, 'deliberately said by Hamlet in order to convince the bystanders of his absolute insanity in all art-matters.' If art be a mirror, we look into it to see— a mask. But more precisely, art is no mirror; it is a 'mist of words,' 'a veil.'

Sometimes the veil is pierced. This indifferent conferral of forms upon life by art may have unexpected consequences which implicate art instead of isolating it. In 'The Decay of Lying' Wilde speaks of 'silly boys who, after reading the adventures of Jack Sheppard or Dick Turpin, pillage the stalls of unfortunate applewomen, break into sweetshops at night, and alarm old gentlemen who are returning home from the city by leaping out on them in suburban lanes, with black masks and unloaded revolvers.' In *Dorian Gray* the effect is more sinister; Dorian declares he has been poisoned by a book, and while Lord Henry assures him that art is too aloof to influence anybody, Dorian is felt to be right. Art may then transmit criminal impulses to its audience. Like Whitman, Wilde could and did say, 'Nor will my poems do good only, they will do just as much evil, perhaps more.'

The artist may be criminal and instill his work with criminality. Wilde's second essay in *Intentions* is 'Pen, Pencil and Poison.' He uses Thomas Wainewright as the type of the artist. We need not expect to find a beautiful soul; Wainewright was instead 'a forger of no mean or ordinary capabilities, and . . . a subtle and secret poisoner almost without rival in this or any age.' Among his interesting tastes, Wainewright had 'that curious love of green, which in individuals is always the sign of a subtle artistic temperament, and in nations is said to denote a laxity, if not a decadence of morals.' When a friend reproached him with a murder, he shrugged his shoulders and gave an answer that Susan Sontag would call camp: 'Yes; it was a dreadful thing to do, but she had very thick ankles.' Wilde concludes that 'the fact of a man being a poisoner is nothing against his prose,' and 'there is no essential incongruity between crime and culture.' Wainewright's criminal career turns out to be strictly relevant to his art, fortifying it and giving it character. The quality of that art is too early to judge, Wilde says, but he clearly believes that Wainewright's personality achieves sufficient criminality to have great artistic promise.

'The Critic as Artist' is the most ambitious of the essays in *Intentions*. It too conveys the notion that art undermines things as they are. The critic is the artist's accomplice in crime, or even masterminds the plot in which they are mutually engaged. Criticism overcomes the tendency of creation to repeat itself; it helps the artist discover unused possibilities. For at bottom, Wilde says, criticism is self-consciousness; it enables us to put our most recent phase at a distance and so go on to another. It disengages us so we may re-engage ourselves in a new way.

From this argument Wilde proceeds to find criticism and self-consciousness to be as necessary as sin. 'What is termed Sin is an essential element of progress'; without it, he holds, the world would stagnate or grow old or become colorless. 'By its curiosity [there is Arnold's word with Wilde's meaning] Sin increases the experience of the race. Through its intensified assertion of individualism it saves us from monotony of type. In its rejection of the current notions about morality, it is one with the highest ethics.' By a dexterous transvaluation of words, Wilde makes

1 4

good and evil exchange places. Even socially sin is far more useful than martyrdom, he says, since it is self-expressive rather than self-repressive. The goal of man is the liberation of personality; when the day of true culture comes, sin will be impossible because the soul will be able to transform 'into elements of a richer experience, or a finer susceptibility, or a newer mode of thought, acts or passions that with the common would be commonplace, or with the uneducated ignoble, or with the shameful vile. Is this dangerous? Yes; it is dangerous—all ideas, as I told you, are so.' What muddies this point of view in Wilde is his looking back to conventional meanings of words like sin, ignoble, and shameful. He is not so ready as Nietzsche to transvaluate these, though he does reshuffle them. His private equation is that sin is the perception of new and dangerous possibilities in action as self-consciousness is in thought and criticism is in art. He espouses individualism, and he encourages society to make individualism more complete than it can be now, and for this reason he sponsors socialism as a communal egotism, like the society made up of separate but equal works of art.

Meantime, before socialism, what should be thought of the criminal impulses of the artist? Increasingly in his later writings, Wilde spreads the guilt from the artist to all men. If we are all insincere, masked, and lying, then the artist is prototype rather than exception. If all the sheep are black, then the artist cannot be blamed for not being white. Such an exculpation is implied in three of Wilde's plays after Salomé—Lady Windermere's Fan, A Woman of No Importance, An Ideal Husband. Wilde allows his characters to be found guilty, but no guiltier than others, and more courageous in their wrongdoing.

Even as he defends them, he allows them to be mildly punished. Half-consciously, Wilde was preparing himself for another abrupt shift in his experience, such as he had made in 1886. It would be false to say that Wilde wanted to go to prison, yet the notion had frequently crossed his mind. He had always associated himself with the poètes maudits, always considered obloquy a certificate of literary merit. In 'The Soul of Man under Socialism' he had opposed suffering, yet acknowledged that the Russian novelists had rediscovered a great medieval theme, the realization of man through suffering. More particularly, in a review of a new book of poems by Wilfrid Scawen Blunt in 1889, he began: 'Prison has had an admirable effect on Mr. Wilfrid Blunt as a poet.' It was like the effect of crime on Wainewright. Blunt had been merely witty and affected earlier, now his work had more depth. 'Mr. Balfour must be praised,' Wilde says jestingly, since 'by sending Mr. Blunt to gaol . . . [he] has converted a clever rhymer into an earnest and deep-thinking poet.' Six years later, just before his own disgrace, Wilde wrote in 'The Soul of Man under Socialism,' 'After all, even in prison a man can be quite free.' These hints indicate that Wilde was prepared, or thought he was, for trial and prison, and expected he would derive artistic profit from them. He had no idea of running away, even on a boyish holiday, whatever his friends might say. Instead he accepted imperial authority as readily as Christ had done—a precedent he discovered for himself, though hardly the first or last in hot water to do so. Blunt's poems written in prison were called *In Vinculis*, and Wilde's letter to Douglas from prison, which we know by Ross's title as *De Profundis*, was originally entitled by Wilde *Epistola: In Carcere et Vinculis*.

Hélas! Wilde's literary career was not transmogrified by prison as he hoped, but his experiences there, which were so much worse than he anticipated, gave him his final theme. As before, he made no effort to exonerate himself by saying that his sins were venial or not sins at all. Defenses of homosexual or 'Uranian' love were common enough at this period; he did not make them. But he reached for the main implication of his disgrace through a double negative; though men thought he was unlike them, he was *not*. He was a genuine scapegoat.

This ultimate conception of himself was never put into an essay, but it is involved in his *De Profundis* letter to Douglas, and in *The Ballad of Reading Gaol*. Both are predictably full of imagery of Christ. Before this Wilde had depreciated pity as a motive in art; now he embraced it. The hero of his poem is a

1 6

man who has murdered his mistress and is about to be hanged for his crime. Wilde identifies himself closely with this prisoner. The poem's tenor is that the prisoners are humanity, all of whom are felons:

> Yet each man kills the thing he loves,
>   By each let this be heard,
> Some do it with a bitter look,
>   Some with a flattering word,
> The coward does it with a kiss,
>   The brave man with a sword! . . .
>
> Some love too little, some too long,
>   Some sell, and others buy;
> Some do the deed with many tears,
>   And some without a sigh:
> For each man kills the thing he loves,
>   Yet each man does not die.

This poem was chosen for the Oxford Book of Modern Verse by Yeats, but he removed what he regarded as the commentary, including these stanzas. His effort to improve the poem evokes sympathy; it must be said however, that whatever the quality of the bare narrative that Yeats prints, for Wilde—as for D. H. Lawrence and most readers—the commentary was the excessive and yet determining part of the poem. During the six years before his imprisonment he had demonstrated first that the artist was basically and usefully criminal, and second that criminality was not confined to artists, but was to be found as commonly among members of the Cabinet. Where most men pretend to a virtue they do not have, the artist, fully aware of his own sins, takes on those they do not acknowledge. The purpose of sin has subtly shifted in Wilde's mind—it is no longer a means for the artist of extending the boundaries of action, it is a means for him to focus and enshrine guilt. He has the courage, exceptional among men, of looking into the heart of things and finding there not brotherly love so much as murder, not self-love so much as suicide. In recognizing the universality of guilt he is like Christ; in revealing his own culpability he plays the role of his own Judas. Wilde, who had written in one of his poems that we are ourselves 'the lips betraying and the life betrayed,' had in fact brought about his own conviction. The result was that he was remarried to the society from which he had divorced himself; he was no outcast, for he accepted and even sought the punishment which other men, equally guilty, would only submit to vicariously through him, just as all the prisoners suffer with the doomed murderer. By means of submission and suffering he gives his life a new purpose, and writes over the palimpsest once again.

In this concern with a social role Wilde has clearly moved away from Pater, and perhaps we can conceive of him as moving towards another writer, Jean Gênet. Gênet is of course ferocious and remorseless in a way that Wilde was not, and makes much less concession to the world. But the two men share an insistence on their own criminality and on a possible sanction for it. The comparison with Christ has been irresistible for both. As Gênet says in *The Thief's Journal*, 'Let us ignore the theologians. "Taking upon Himself the sins of the world" means exactly this: experiencing potentially and in their effects all sins; it means having subscribed to evil. Every creator must thus shoulder—the expression seems feeble—must make his own, to the point of knowing it to be his substance, circulating in his arteries, the evil given by him, which his heroes choose freely.' And again, Gênet speaks like Wilde of the courage required to do wrong, saying: 'If he has courage, the guilty man decides to be what crime has made him.' He wishes to obtain 'the recognition of evil.' Both writers envisage a regeneration which can come only from total assumption of their proclivities and their lot; as Gênet puts it: 'I shall destroy appearances, the casings will burn away and one evening I shall appear there, in the palm of your hand, quiet and pure, like a glass statuette. You will see me. Round about me there will be nothing left.' Wilde summons for this sacred moment a red rose growing from the hanged man's mouth, a white one from his heart. He had terrified André Gide by trying to persuade that strictly reared young man to authorize evil, as to some extent in the *acte gratuit* Gide did, and it is just such authorization that Gênet asserts with more fierceness than Wilde.

In his criticism and in his work generally, Wilde balanced two ideas which, we have observed, look contradictory. One is that art is disengaged from actual life, the other that it is deeply incriminated with it. The first point of view is sometimes taken by Yeats, though only to qualify it, the second without qualification by Gênet. That art is sterile, and that it is infectious, are attitudes not beyond reconciliation. Wilde never formulated their union, but he implied something like this: by its creation of beauty art reproaches the world, calling attention to the world's faults through their very omission; so the sterility of art is an affront or a parable. Art may also outrage the world by flouting its laws or by picturing indulgently their violation. Or art may seduce the world by making it follow an example which seems bad but is discovered to be better than it seems. In these various ways the artist forces the world towards self-recognition, with at least a tinge of self-redemption.

Yet this ethical or almost ethical view of art coexists in Wilde with its own cancellation. He could write *Salomé* with one hand, dwelling upon incest and necrophilia, and show them as self-defeated, punished by execution and remorse. With the other hand, he could dissolve by the critical intellect all notions of sin and guilt. He does so in *The Importance of Being Earnest* which is all insouciance where *Salomé* is all incrimination. In *The Importance of Being Earnest* sins which are presented as accursed in *Salomé* and unnameable in *Dorian Gray* are translated into a different key, and appear as Algernon's inordinate and selfish craving for—cucumber sandwiches. The substitution of mild gluttony for fearsome lechery renders all vice harmless. There *is* a wicked brother, but he is just our old friend Algernon. The double life which is so serious a matter for Dorian or for the Ideal Husband, becomes a harmless Bunburying, or playing Jack in the country and Ernest in town. In the earlier, four-act version of the play, Wilde even parodied punishment, by having a bailiff come to take Jack to Holloway Prison (as Wilde himself was soon to be taken) not for homosexuality, but for running up food bills at the Savoy. Jack is disinclined, he says, to be imprisoned in the suburbs for dining in town, and makes out a cheque. The notion of expiation is also mocked; as Cecily observes: 'They have been eating muffins. That looks like repentance.' Finally, the theme of regeneration is parodied in the efforts of Ernest and Jack to be baptized. (By the way, in the earlier version Prism is also about to be baptized, and someone comments, 'To be born again would be of considerable advantage to her.') The ceremonial unmasking at the play's end, which had meant death for Dorian Gray, leaves everyone barefaced for a new puppet show, that of matrimony. Yet amusing as it all is, much of the comedy derives from Wilde's own sense of the realities of what are being mocked. He was in only momentary refuge from his more usual cycle which ran from scapegrace to scapegoat.

During his stay in prison Wilde took up the regeneration theme in *De Profundis* and after being freed he resumed it in *The Ballad of Reading Gaol*. But he was too self-critical not to find the notion of rebirth a little preposterous. When his friends complained of his resuming old habits, he said, 'A patriot put in prison for loving his country, loves his country, and a poet in prison for loving boys, loves boys.' But to write about himself as unredeemed, unpunished, unreborn, to claim that his sins were nothing, that his form of love was more noble than most other people's, that what had happened to him was the result merely of legal obtuseness, was impossible for Wilde. So long as he had been a scapegrace the door to comedy was still open; once having accepted the role of scapegoat the door was closed. He conceived of a new play, but it was in his earlier mode and he could not write it. Cramped to one myth, and that sombre and depleted, Wilde could not extricate himself. There was nothing to do but die, which accordingly he did. But not without one final assertion of a past enthusiasm: he was converted to Catholicism just before his death.

Note: Quotations from letters are taken from *The Letters of Oscar Wilde*, ed. Rupert Hart-Davis (London and New York, 1962).

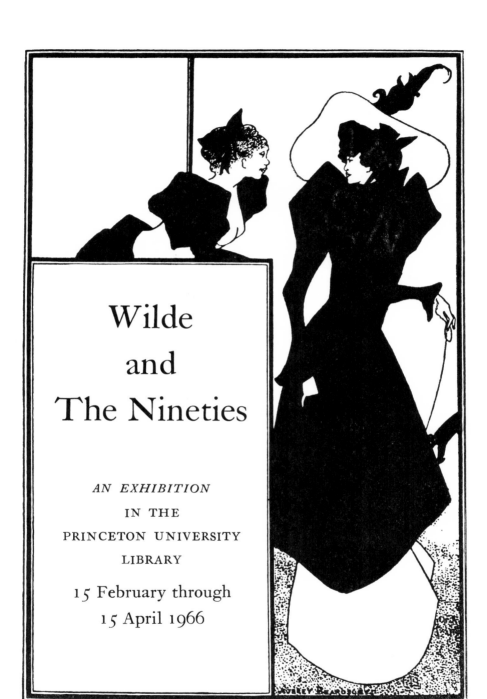

Wilde
and
The Nineties

AN *EXHIBITION*

IN THE

PRINCETON UNIVERSITY

LIBRARY

15 February through
15 April 1966

*Aubrey Beardsley's original drawing for the design
reproduced on the obverse of this page is in the Princeton University
Library. Created in 1894 as a poster, it was first published with
Beardsley's article 'The Art of the Hoarding' in the
issue of* THE NEW REVIEW *for July 1894.*

THE EIGHTEEN NINETIES:
PERSPECTIVES

E. D. H. JOHNSON

ATTITUDES towards the 1890's in England vary as widely as the points of view from which the period can be regarded. To the lover of things Victorian it marks the rather inglorious decline of an epoch. Arnold, Browning, and Newman had died in 1888, 1889, and 1890 respectively. To all intents and purposes the careers of Ruskin and Swinburne were over in 1889; and it only remained for Tennyson's death in 1892 to ring down the curtain on an age of giants. The years immediately following would discredit the two great aesthetic traditions which had sustained the literary activity of the preceding century. Public reaction to the Wilde trial in 1895 repudiated the theory that the imagination is autonomous, subject solely to the laws of artistic creation; and the political disillusionment growing out of the Boer War made a mockery of the Utopian pretension that art can mould society.

When the Nineties are viewed as the prelude to the twentieth rather than the aftermath of the nineteenth century, very different patterns emerge. Attention shifts to the figures who, having served their literary apprenticeship in those years, outgrew, as we like to think, early affinities, and went on to better things. And so we are disposed to treat Shaw, Yeats, and Conrad as our own contemporaries and to take full credit for their major achievements in drama, poetry, and the novel.

While these perspectives incorporate a measure of truth, they leave the impression that the *fin de siècle* was a purely transitional period, lacking intrinsic significance. Unfortunately, the Nineties have not been much better served by the host of studies devoted exclusively to that decade. In common acceptance of the term, Decadence still carries with it overtones of perversity and sensationalism; and though one would suppose the shock value to have been exhausted, critics continue to concern themselves with the lives rather than the works of the writers and artists whom Yeats called The Tragic Generation. Any doubts that the closing years of the nineteenth century were a time of widely varied creativity and that this consideration is paramount should be dispelled by the present exhibition.

The title, *Wilde and the Nineties,* is no misnomer. Although Wilde was certainly the most flamboyant figure of his day, he never thought of himself as a professional *littérateur*; and it may come as something of a surprise that he was not more closely associated with the coteries and movements which set the aesthetic tone of the times. He did not belong to the Rhymers' Club; he never contributed to *The Yellow Book* or *The Savoy*; and he was not really very intimate with any of the leading literary figures among his contemporaries. Yet, the examples which Mr. and Mrs. Donald F. Hyde have lent to this exhibition from their magnificent collection of Wilde papers, manuscripts, and books, when ranged against Princeton's extensive holdings in all aspects of the Nineties, show that Wilde's career impinged on the literary nerve-centers of his age at every point. Whether as poet, dramatist, writer of fiction, or critic, his work, in fact, epitomizes the spirit of that age.

Despite the perennial fascination of the Nineties, there has been no very successful attempt to define its distinctive character. It stands in relation to the Aesthetic Movement of the 1870's and 1880's in somewhat the same relation as the Rococo to the Baroque. Its effort was less to develop new expressive forms than to refine and embellish received motifs. It is perhaps best described as a final efflorescence of the romantic sensibility, ignited by the example of the French symbolists and naturalists with whom their English compeers had so many and such close ties.

But these influences will hardly explain the strange uniformity within heterogeneity that sets the achievement of the *fin de siècle* apart from anything that came before or after. This inner consistency is a matter of tone or style rather than of shared themes and techniques; it relates primarily to the temper of mind which ties together the extraordinary diversity of creative activity here represented.

The end of the nineteenth century in England released in artists a kind of rage for experience, a passionate need to expend their energies, as if these individuals had in very fact foreseen the early deaths in store for so many of them. Shaw might have been their spokesman when in the Epistle Dedicatory to *Man and Superman* he described 'the true joy of life' as 'being thoroughly worn out before you are thrown on the scrap heap.' This 'hunger of the imagination,' in Samuel Johnson's phrase, weighed an insatiable curiosity to savor the untried against a mocking, even cynical irreverence for the old and the outworn. It was prevailingly iconoclastic, partly out of delight in the pure gesture of revolt, but also from a very real need to transcend the stale conventionality, the hermetic smugness and hypocrisy of a society immured in bourgeois values.

As associated with the concept of Decadence, the spirit of the age is most apparent in the rather hectic and overstrained exoticism of the cenacle of poets which included Ernest Dowson and Arthur Symons. But the same restlessly probing vitality informs writing which has better stood the test of time: the mordant comedies, for example, by which Shaw and Wilde awakened theatrical audiences from a century of lethargy; or the novels of Hardy and Moore, which daringly used the clinical methods of naturalism to lay bare the nether world. The flight from boredom, inspired in part by contempt for middle-class conformity, helps explain the popularity of other literary forms which exploited the *outré* imaginative resources of the period: the early science fiction of H. G. Wells; the adventure stories of Kipling and Rider Haggard with their appeal to the sense of Empire; psychological thrillers in the vein of du Maurier's *Trilby* and Wilde's *The Picture of Dorian Gray*; and finally, Conan Doyle's detective yarns about Sherlock Holmes, that most inveterate of Bohemians in private life!

For all the exuberance of Shaw, the wit of Wilde, the urbane spoofery of Max Beerbohm, the best writing of the Nineties is permeated with melancholy. This mood was a legacy of the enlightened hedonism which Pater had championed so effectively. 'The splendour of experience' cannot hide 'its awful brevity.' Yet, the human protest against impermanence is still to seek to exist with the greatest possible intensity in each passing instant; and the creator, especially, opposes his artifact to the unceasing flux. Thus it is that the best *fin-de-siècle* art impressionistically records the poignancy of fleeting moods. Symons spoke of 'this endeavour after a perfect truth to one's impression, to one's intuition.' The lyric, the Wildean epigram, the short story, the sketch, and the dialogue—these are the modes which most vividly embody the temper of an age obsessed with mutability.

Yet, if their inspiration was sporadic, these artists were tireless craftsmen; and their insistence on formal perfection produced a uniform brilliance of style which disarms criticism of the too frequent triviality of content. Not since the seventeenth century has there been so brilliant a gathering of minor poets. Translators and imitators of the complex verse patterns of Baudelaire and his followers among the symbolists, they imparted new elegance and precision to lyric poetry; and the sensitive ear delights to discriminate between the different voices which rang modulations on a few well-worn themes. To Symons' colloquial ease and insouciance is opposed the twilit nostalgia of Dowson; John Davidson's gnarled speech rhythms contrast to Lionel Johnson's austerity of tone; already in the early Yeats there is more than a hint of that matchlessly controlled violence; and Wilde out of suffering achieves a new and moving lucidity in *The Ballad of Reading Gaol*. In *Art Poétique* Verlaine, whom the Decadents loved above all other French poets, distilled the fugitive beauty and freshness which graces the best lyrics of the Nineties:

> De la musique encore et toujours!
> Que ton vers soit la chose envolée
> Qu'on sent qui fuit d'une âme en allée
> Vers d'autres cieux à d'autres amours.

Que ton vers soit la bonne aventure
Éparse au vent crispé du matin
Qui va fleurant la menthe et le thym . . .
Et tout le reste est littérature.

And in after years Yeats wrote the epitaph of his youthful asso-
ciates who, whatever their lives, never compromised the purity
of their art:

You had to face your ends when young—
'Twas wine or women, or some curse—
But never made a poorer song
That you might have a heavier purse,
Nor gave loud service to a cause
That you might have a troop of friends.
You kept the Muses' sterner laws,
And unrepenting faced your ends.

Despite its intransigent resistance to social pressures, the artistic life of the Nineties was to a surprising degree a communal
enterprise. Without the sympathetic and tolerant support of
such publishers as John Lane, Elkin Mathews, and Leonard
Smithers, the movement would never have taken shape and acquired the lustre that for a few years made London the rival of
Paris in the world of arts and letters. Furthermore, there has
never been a period when literature was so closely wedded to the
sister arts. In 1892 William Morris revived the craft of fine
bookmaking at his Kelmscott Press; and his lead was followed
by Charles Ricketts at the Vale Press and Emery Walker at the
Doves Press. The limited editions of contemporary writers, as
well as the illustrated editions of classics, designed by these
masters remain a lasting delight to the eye and hand of the
bibliophile.

The Nineties, finally, was the golden age for little magazines.
The astonishing proliferation of these publications is very fully
represented in this exhibition, from *The Spirit Lamp*, which
Lord Alfred Douglas edited as an undergraduate at Oxford, and

The Pagan Review, for the sole number of which William Sharp wrote all the pieces under different pseudonyms, to *The Yellow Book* and *The Savoy,* of which Aubrey Beardsley was art editor. Had nothing else survived, the Nineties would live on in the varied contents of these beautifully designed periodicals. Not only did they help make the reputation of nearly every writer who came to prominence in that thronged period, but they also enabled the great draughtsmen of the day, such as Beardsley and Phil May, to perfect black-and-white illustration. To turn the pages of *The Yellow Book* or *The Savoy* is to recapture the best moments of an all too brief decade passionately dedicated to the faith that life is meant to be lived in the spirit of art.

Oscar Wilde at the time of the first production of
THE IMPORTANCE OF BEING EARNEST, February 1895. Hyde Collection.

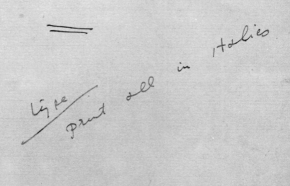

Wilde's manuscript of 'Helas!', epitaph for both the 1881 and 1892 editions of his POEMS. J. Harlin O'Connell Collection, Princeton University Library.

What book is it? Lhs!
352.

(1)

Function
the ~~~~~ & Criticism: A Dialogue.

Scene. A young man's rooms in
Piccadilly.

Persons. Gilbert and Ernest.

___

Gilbert (at the piano) My dear
Ernest! what are you laughing
at?

Ernest. I am laughing at a capital
story in the last ~~~~~~~~ Reminiscences..
Gilbert. How can you read modern
memoirs? They are usually produced
by people who have either entirely
lost their memories, or have never
done anything worth recording. You
had much better let me play
Chopin to you, or play you a fantasy by Dvorak. Shall I
play you Dvorak. He writes passionate,
curiously-coloured things.

Ernest. No: I don't want music just
at present. It is far too indefinite. Besides,
I took the Baroness Bernstein down to dinner last
night, and, though she was perfectly charming in
every other respect, she insisted on discussing
music as if it was actually
written in the German language. Now,
whatever music sounds like I am glad to say that it does
not, sound, like German. There are
forms of patriotism that are really
absolutely degrading. Don't play any
more, Gilbert. Turn round, and talk

Dear Mr. Mathews.

I enclose agreement for Mr. Gray's poems. Will you let me have agreement for Sphinx — I was so busy before leaving town I could not call. Sincerely yours

Oscar Wilde

51. Kaiser Friedrichs Promenade
Bad-Homburg.

Elkin Mathews
&
John Lane,
Publishers & Vendors of Choice
and Rare Editions in
Belles Lettres.

The · Bodley · Head.
VIGO STREET,
LONDON, W.

17ᵗʰ June 92

To Oscar Wilde, Esq.
Dear Sir,

Silverpoints [Poems] by John Gray.
We agree to issue the above book in the autumn on your undertaking the cost of the designs — block for same — paper, printing and binding of an edition, not exceeding 250 copies.

In advertising the above, at your charge, we undertake not to exceed the sum of

Of the Honey Child, and of each turn around.
Mishka! screamed a mad bird's note
Deep in the sky when around his throat
The triple coil of her hair she wound.
She strokes his limbs with a humming sound

Mishka is white like a hunter's son
For he knows no more of the ancient south
When the Honey Child's lips are upon his mouth
When all her kisses are joined in one
And his body is bathed in grass & sun

The shadows lie purple beneath the trees
And flecks of mauve where the finches pass
Leap in the stalks of the deep rank grass
Flutter of wing and the buzz of bees
Deepen the silence and sweeten ease

The Honey Child is an olive tree
The voice of ... the voice of flowers
East of them all, and all the hours
The Honey Child is a winged bee
Her touch is a perfumed melody

yrs ever Dorian

The last page of John Gray's letter of 9 January 1891 to Oscar Wilde ending with Gray's poem 'The Honey Child' and signed 'Dorian.' Hyde Collection.

Wilde's letter (upper left) to Elkin Mathews enclosing an 'agreement for Mr. Gray's poems.' Hyde Collection.

The first page (lower left) of the agreement of 17 June 1892 for SILVERPOINTS, signed by Mathews and Lane and by Wilde. Princeton University Library.

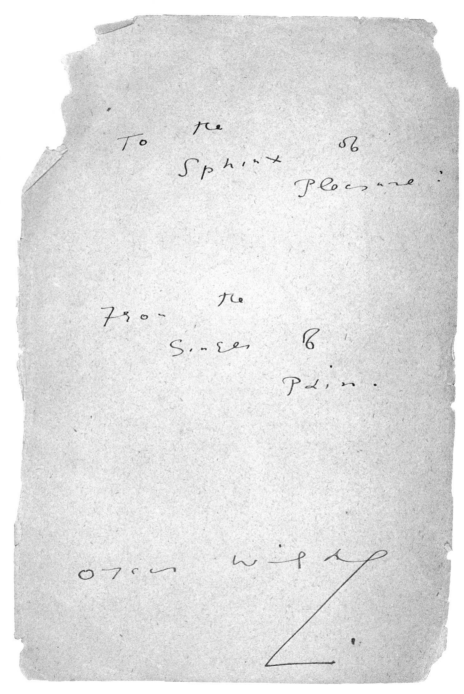

Wilde's inscription to Ada Leverson in the 1898 French edition of
THE BALLAD OF READING GAOL: 'To the Sphinx of Pleasure: From the Singer of Pain.'
Princeton University Library.

The cover, in Charles Ricketts' gilt and vellum design, of THE SPHINX.
Princeton University Library.

a delight to me
that I constantly
take it up, and
always find it
stimulating and
refreshing: Enclosed
is the land of
intellectual force
but you have done
much to clear
the air: we
are both Celtic,
and I like to
think that we are

friends: For
these and many
other reasons Salomé
presents herself
to you in purple
raiment.

Pray accept
her with my best
wishes,

and Believe me
very truly yours
Oscar Wilde.

The last two pages of Wilde's letter, postmarked 23 February 1893, to George Bernard Shaw, which begins: 'You have written well and wisely and with sound wit on the ridiculous institution of a stage-censorship: your little book on Ibsenism and Ibsen is such a delight to me that I constantly take it up. . . .'
Robert H. Taylor Collection.

From Oscar

To the gilt-mailed
Boy.

POEMS.

at Oxford,

in the heart
of June.

Wilde's inscription in the copy of the 1892 edition of his POEMS which he presented
to Lord Alfred Douglas. Robert H. Taylor Collection.

Oscar Wilde

« Butchered to make an English holiday. »

en 7 { « Livré aux bouchers pour offrir un divertissement à l'Angleterre »

« Prison d'Holloway — Lundi soir. »

Mon très cher enfant,

Que ceci vous assure de mon immortel, de mon éternel amour pour vous. Demain tout sera fini. Si la prison et le deshonneur devaient être ma destinée, pensez que mon amour pour vous et l'idée, cette croyance plus divine encore, que vous m'aimez en retour, me soutiendront dans mon malheur et me rendront capable, je l'espère, de supporter ma peine très patiemment. L'espoir, mieux que cela, la certitude de vous rencontrer encore dans quelque monde, étant le but et l'encouragement de ma vie présente, ah! je dois dans ce monde-ci, continuer à vivre.

---

(1) Après la publication, dans notre numéro d'août, de l'article de M. Hugues Rebell = Défense d'Oscar Wilde, Lord Alfred Douglas nous écrivit pour nous demander si nous serions disposés à insérer un article de lui sur l'affaire Oscar Wilde. Ayant accepté, nous avons reçu le document de haut intérêt psychologique qu'on va lire. Nous donnons en appendice le texte original des lettres et passages de lettres d'Oscar Wilde que Lord Alfred Douglas a intercalés dans son article. — N. d. l. R.

The first page of the only known copy of the text, in an unknown hand, of Lord Alfred Douglas's unpublished article written in defense of Wilde in August 1895. It includes the only surviving texts of a number of Wilde's letters to Douglas. Princeton University Library.

To the right is the first page of Wilde's note, written at the moment of his arrest on 2 April 1895, to Lord Alfred Douglas. It continues: 'Would you ask Percy, and George Alexander, and Waller, at the Haymarket, to attend to give bail. Would you also wire Humphreys to appear at Bow Street for me. Wire to 41 Norfolk Square, W. Also, come to see me. Ever yours Oscar.' Hyde Collection.

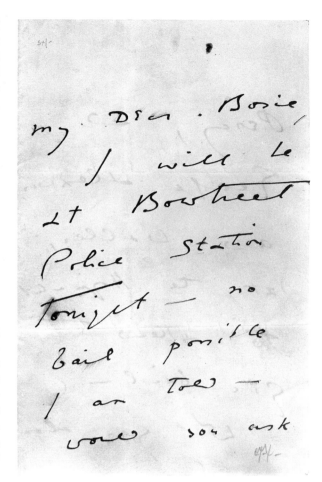

Below is Wilde's now-faint pencil notation on the face of an envelope— 'Bosie's Father is going to make a Scene tonight/ I am going to stop him'—of the Marquis of Queensberry's attempt to discredit Wilde by addressing the first night audience of THE IMPORTANCE OF BEING EARNEST on 14 February 1895. Hyde Collection.

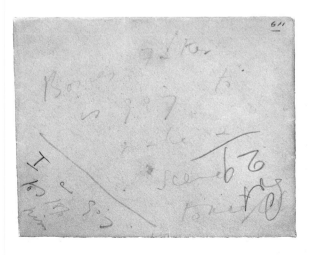

On the overleaf are two pages from Max Beerbohm's copy of Richard Le Gallienne's LIMITED EDITIONS (1892) bearing the artist's caricatures of the author and of Oscar Wilde and a parody of Beardsley's black-and-white style. Robert H. Taylor Collection. →

verb. There is no telling how we would value many of our possessions if they were more arduously come by: our relatives, our husbands and wives, our presentation poetry from the unpoetical, our invitation cards to one-man shows in Bond Street, the auto-photographs of great actors, the flatteries of the unimportant, the attentions of the embarrassing—how might we value all such treasures if they were, so to say, restricted to a limited issue, and guaranteed 'not to be reprinted,' 'plates destroyed and type distributed.'

9

INDEED, all nature is on the side of limited editions. Make a thing cheap, she cries from every

of night we forget beneath the mimic firmament of the music-hall. ✳

ONLY in the lamplit closet of the bookman, the fanatic of first and fine editions, is it remembered and revered. To him alone of an Americanised, 'pirated-edition,' reading world, the book remains the sacred thing it is. Therefore, he would not have it degraded by, so to say, an indiscriminate breeding, such as has also made the children of men cheap and vulgar to each other. We pity the desert rose that is born to unappreciated beauty, the unset gem that glitters on no woman's hand; but what of the book that eats its heart out in the threepenny

4

THE EXHIBITION:
A RETROSPECTIVE VIEW

ALFRED L. BUSH

Selections from the Oscar Wilde collection formed by Mr. and Mrs. Donald F. Hyde at Four Oaks Farm in Somerville, New Jersey, comprised the unifying thread in the Princeton University Library's exhibition of early spring 1966: 'Wilde and the Nineties.' The larger context of the period was built around these materials, with further items to exemplify Wilde's accomplishment and to represent the achievement of his contemporaries in the decade. This was possible by drawing on the collections of the University Library and that of Mr. Robert H. Taylor of Princeton. The University's holdings for this period are chiefly in the J. Harlin O'Connell Collection of the Literature of the 1890's, which was acquired by the University in 1958 through the generosity of Mr. O'Connell's daughter, Mrs. Pierre Matisse; and the A. E. Gallatin Beardsley Collection which Mr. Gallatin presented to the Library in 1948. The Beardsley Collection was sparsely represented only because the major portion of this Collection was, at the time of the exhibition, on its way to London where it will form part of the Beardsley retrospective exhibition at the Victoria and Albert Museum early this summer. The University's Morris L. Parrish Collection of Victorian Novelists, the Theatre Collection, and the Graphic Arts Collection also contributed important items which made it possible to represent more fully the fiction and drama of the period.*

PRECURSORS

Most of the art and many of the personalities of the 1890's reached back to the preceding epoch. In the opening case of the exhibition a fading photograph [Taylor] in which Oscar

---

* Materials in the exhibition, not otherwise designated in this essay, are in the collections of the Princeton University Library. Titles of printed books, pamphlets, and periodicals which were exhibited are given in small capitals.

Wilde and George Meredith relax in an English garden, visually superimposed the two eras. And the exhibition of the later works of the four giants of the previous literary era whose lives and art extended into the decade, led viewers from the end of one literary milieu into the vigorous beginnings of another: Meredith's THE AMAZING MARRIAGE (1895) and its author's letter [Taylor] of September 1891 in which he speaks of having 'tried to show, in a sort of preface to "The Egoist," that comedy works by a different method & produces an effect on the mind, as positive as the Realistic. . . . neither in that book nor in any other of my books will artificial dialogue or any Phantasia of writing be found when warm human emotion comes into play'; the manuscript of Swinburne's *The Bride's Tragedy,* the first edition of his OTHER POEMS (1894), and THE TALE OF BALEN (1896) bearing a long presentation to his brother; the copy of Walter Pater's AN IMAGINARY PORTRAIT [Hyde] inscribed from Oscar Wilde to his wife, Constance, in July 1894; Tennyson's THE FORESTERS, published in the year of the Poet Laureate's death in 1892 and inscribed to Helen Allingham. All of these were presided over by Max Beerbohm's watercolor caricature [Taylor] of Tennyson declaiming 'In Memoriam' to the widowed Queen Victoria in a vast palace room whose walls bear a design of skulls and crossbones.

THEATRE

The portion of the exhibition which was devoted to the theatre was dominated by Wilde and George Bernard Shaw. The dramatic renaissance which had its origin in the 7 June 1889 performance of Ibsen's *A Doll's House* and the 1891 performances of his *Ghosts* and *Hedda Gabler* were brought to mind by a copy of one of the seminal books of the decade: Shaw's THE QUINTESSENCE OF IBSENISM (1891) and a letter [Taylor] written in late February of 1893 in which Wilde addresses Shaw: '. . . your little book on Ibsenism and Ibsen is such a delight to me that I constantly take it up, and always find it stimulating and refreshing: . . . we are both Celtic, and I like to think that we are friends.'

The original editions of Shaw's PLAYS PLEASANT AND UN-PLEASANT (1898) and WIDOWERS' HOUSES (1893) shared space with playbills from the first performances of WIDOWERS' HOUSES and ARMS AND THE MAN—the latter surprising in its incidental announcement that the performance of Shaw's play would be preceded by the performance of 'a New and Original Play . . . The Land of Heart's Desire by W. B. Yeats.' The copy of WIDOWERS' HOUSES which was displayed was one of the rare issues of the first edition in blue cloth which Shaw himself in later life commented on: 'What puzzles me about this copy is its blue cover. Henry & Co. published it in a green coloured cloth case of the shade called citrine. When Henry & Co. honourably retired in due course, they very magnanimously presented me with the unsold and unbound remainder of this edition: and I had this remainder bound for myself in mauve cloth to distinguish it from the old copies. And . . . now . . . comes along . . . the blue copy. . . . I never saw or heard of any blue copies. . . . I deny its existence . . . .' Shaw's denial would have been made all the more difficult had he been confronted with the copy [Taylor] included in this exhibition for it bears an inscription to the artist Bertha Newcombe written by Shaw himself and dated in May 1893—very shortly after the book was published.

While none of the ten plays which Shaw wrote in the Nineties proved a popular success, his influence in that decade was immense. By his plays and by his dramatic criticism in THE SATURDAY REVIEW and elsewhere, he made himself one of the dominant theatrical forces in London. The exhibition included the July 1894 issue of THE NEW REVIEW in which Shaw set forth his dramatic credo in 'A Dramatic Realist to His Critics,' and THE SATURDAY REVIEW of 23 February 1895 opened to Shaw's criticism, in a single essay, of THE IMPORTANCE OF BEING EARNEST, Pinero's THE SECOND MRS. TANQUERAY and, even more char-

33

acteristic of his unconventional reviewing, his notice of '? A play in ? acts. By ?'.

Playbills of the opening performance of 27 May 1893, a photograph of that production, and a copy of its first publication in 1895, presented THE SECOND MRS. TANQUERAY, which many critics have recognized as the work in which the English drama at the close of the nineteenth century first surely found itself, and to which the English stage owes its later prevailing tendency towards naturalism. The copy of the first edition of the play was opened to the frontispiece—a photograph of the author which could be reassuringly compared with the exaggerations of the caricature in watercolors by Max Beerbohm which hung above it.

Sharing the case with Pinero was Wilde's THE IMPORTANCE OF BEING EARNEST. Wilde cut short a holiday in Algeria with Lord Alfred Douglas early in 1895 to hurry back to London by himself for the opening of this play on 14 February. There he discovered that Douglas's father, the Marquis of Queensberry, was plotting to address the first night audience to discredit him. It was sometime that evening that Wilde scrawled, on the envelope [Hyde] displayed in the exhibition: 'Bosie's Father is going to make a scene tonight. I am going to stop him.' Twenty policemen guarded the theatre when the 'Scarlet Marquis' arrived and prevented his entering it. This incident did as much as anything to precipitate the case of Wilde v. Queensberry. The frustration of his plot and the immense success of Wilde's play drove Queensberry to call, four days later, at Wilde's club to leave the card which had such grave consequences.

Near this dramatic note were playbills from this performance, one of them autographed by the playwright; an album of photographs [Hyde] of the original performance; copy number one [Hyde] of the limited issue of the first edition bearing 'Mr. Pollitt's Bookplate,' designed by Aubrey Beardsley for Herbert C. Pollitt; and a second copy [Hyde] of the first edition inscribed to Louis Wilkinson and sent under cover of a letter of 3 February 1899, in which Wilde wrote of the play as 'a fanciful, absurd, comedy, written when I was playing with that tiger Life. I hope it will amuse you.' Wilde's first letter to Wilkinson, written a year earlier, was also exhibited [Hyde]. 'Certainly: you can dramatise my play, but please tell me if the version is yours, and how the play is constructed.' This was Wilde's response to Wilkinson's proposal for a dramatization of THE PICTURE OF DORIAN GRAY. Wilkinson, who was a seventeen-year-old Radley student at the time, later admitted that he invented an 'Ipswich Dramatic Society'; its desire to dramatize Wilde's novel was a means of getting into correspondence with Wilde whose work he admired. Wilde continued to exchange letters with him for the rest of his life, though the two never met. Two other letters in the exhibition concerned the drama. In one [Hyde] he asks that Henley and Stevenson's plays be sent to him at Babbacombe Cliff 'where I am for the winter' and where, early in 1893, he wrote much of A Woman of No Importance. And in the other [Hyde], as Sebastian Melmoth, a pseudonym Wilde assumed for his correspondence after being released from prison, he explores the possibility of collaborating on a play with Kyrle Bellew in 1899.

Wilde's sketches for parts of 'A Florentine Tragedy' [Hyde], opened to pages where Wilde's cancellations and revisions are elaborated with a marginal drawing of the profile of a bearded figure with a nimbus, are surviving fragments of the author's attempt to rewrite in 1897 a play first outlined by him in 1883.

Three copies [Hyde] of the first edition of AN IDEAL HUSBAND chronicled both the origin of the play and its publication. One bears an inscription by Frank Harris with his version of the play's inception: 'I thought of a drama on the subject and told it to Oscar Wilde who used the story in this play.' A second has tipped in a letter to the publisher proposing an alternative dedication, shown in manuscript, to read: 'To Frank Harris/ The compensation for Injustice is, /that in that dark Ordeal we gather the worthiest around us.' The book appeared with the dedication reading: 'To Frank Harris/ A Slight Tribute to his power and distinction as an artist/ his chivalry and nobility as a friend.' The third copy is inscribed by Wilde to Robert Ross, 'The perfect friend,' and recalls one of the most enduring of Wilde's friendships. Ross first met Wilde in 1886, remained one of his most loyal friends, was with him at his death, and became his literary executor.

LADY WINDERMERE'S FAN, the first of Wilde's plays to be produced in England, received special attention in the exhibition which coincided with a new staging of the play by the University's repertory company at McCarter Theatre. A copy of the first appearance of the play in book form, in November 1893 [Hyde]; playbills of the original performance at the St. James's Theatre on 20 February 1892, and a production photograph, in the July 1892 issue of THE THEATRE, which depicts George Alexander in the role of Lord Windermere, were the setting for two letters [Hyde] from Wilde to Alexander, who also was the original producer. In these the author of the play gives his first 'Lord Windermere' extensive directions on how to shape the original performance.

The materials relating to the earliest production of the play were juxtaposed with the playbill and sketches, by Barbara Miller and Charles Blackburn, of settings and costumes for its most recent performance: that which opened at Princeton's McCarter Theatre on 18 February 1966, just two days short of the 74th anniversary of the play's original performance.

Wilde's plays were not unique in their departure from realistic method. J. M. Barrie, in works such as THE LITTLE MINISTER, also avoided the exact imitation of life by employing older burlesque methods to produce a new romance. A copy of the first edition of this novel (1891) was exhibited with three views from the original London performance of its stage version, and with playbills from both the first British and American productions. The New York opening, in October 1897, preceded the English performances by one month and starred Maude Adams.

The more popular—and now forgotten—drama of the decade, which was frequently an incompetent reflection of the stronger theatrical tradition which Barrie represents, was recalled in the exhibition by a playbill of performances of *Dream Faces* by Wynn Miller and *A Pair of Spectacles* 'adapted from the French by Sydney Grundy.' At the same time that the higher drama of the Nineties was going through its 'off-Broadway' era, the popular theatre thrived. Shaw wrote in 1897 in THE SATURDAY REVIEW: 'If every manager considers it due to himself to produce nothing cheaper than *The Prisoner of Zenda*, not to mention the splendours of the Lyceum, then good-bye to high dramatic art. The managers will, perhaps, retort that, if high dramatic art means Ibsen, then they ask for nothing better than to get rid of it. I am too polite to reply, bluntly, that high dramatic art *does* mean Ibsen; that Ibsen's plays are at this moment the head of the dramatic body; and that though an actor manager can, and often does, do without a head, dramatic art cannot.' Photographs of George Alexander as Prince Rudolf in the original performance of *The Prisoner of Zenda* were exhibited with the playbill of the first performance.

In a decade striving toward a naturalistic theatre, there were many attempts at escape. The majestic solemnity of Tennyson's plays, such as *Becket* which opened on 6 February 1893 (represented in the exhibition by the playbill of the first production, a lavishly illustrated SOUVENIR OF BECKET, and a photograph of Henry Irving in the title role), owed their success not to any inherent virtue but to a combination of the author's poetic fame and the equally popular acting of Irving, who starred in most of them. Out of the sentimental pieces that Pinero wrote toward the end of the decade came only one drama of significance, *Trelawny of the 'Wells,'* first staged in January 1898 in a production whose playbill was included in the exhibition.

It was in the previous decade that the satire of Gilbert and Sullivan's *Patience* kept alive an interest in Wilde that he might not have otherwise sustained. But only two productions of these collaborators appeared for the first time in the Nineties— their *Utopia, Limited* and THE GRAND DUKE. Neither of these operettas had the popularity of their predecessors and were

3 7

dropped from the D'Oyly Carte repertory. The playbill of the original performance of *Utopia, Limited* and the program and book for THE GRAND DUKE [Taylor] were displayed.

The program [Taylor] and privately-printed prompt book of Henry James's THE AMERICAN, the author's dramatization of his 1877 novel of the same title, were printed in 1891. The play ran for 70 performances from its first night, 26 September 1891, at the Opera Comique in London, but the text of the dramatic version, as shown in the exhibition, was never formally published in book form during the author's life.

In 1889 while still teaching at Greenock, John Davidson issued his privately printed PLAYS, which the exhibition included. The book is a rarity in any form, but this copy has the added interest of possessing not only the original title page but also a second title page inserted when the stock was taken over by Elkin Mathews in 1893. Though it was his poetry that first won him distinction among his contemporaries, it was to drama that Davidson devoted most of his writing in the early part of his career. The prompt book of FOR THE CROWN, Davidson's translation of François Coppée's play *Pour la Couronne,* and a stack of correspondence with John Lane concerning his PLAYS and other dramas were also exhibited.

Few poets of the period did not try their hand temporarily at drama. Representing this tentative activity were the manuscript, dated April 1893, of Maurice Hewlett's drama *Simonetta in Florence* and some of the rarer dramatic imprints of the decade: André Raffalovich's ROSES OF SHADOW ('Privately printed and not for distribution'); Hewlett's PAN AND THE YOUNG SHEPHERD in a trial binding of decorated green cloth which the author objected to, with the result that very few copies in the original form, like that exhibited, are known; and Michael Field's A QUESTION OF MEMORY, published in 1893 as part of the Independent Theatre. The activity of the latter was suggested by a program announcing the third season with plays scheduled by Field, Todhunter, Besant and Pollock, Ibsen, Zola, Strindberg, and Shaw.

It was in the portion of the exhibition on drama that Phil May was introduced by his sketch of 'A theatrical bar,' which he drew in 1892 just after returning from Paris to London and to an established reputation as one of the finest pen draftsmen of his time. Before him were innumerable contributions to papers and journals of the decade and, in 1896, a position on the staff of PUNCH as the undisputed king of pictorial humorists. So severe a critic as Whistler said: 'Modern Black and White Art could be summed up in two words—Phil May.' A final touch of humor and color was given this section by Max Beerbohm's drawing of Stephen Phillips, the one-time actor turned poet and dramatist.

POETRY

Three copies of Wilde's POEMS, 1892 (the only edition to appear in the Nineties: the cover, title page and half title were newly designed by Ricketts, but the text itself was made up from unsold sheets of the last of five editions of 250 copies produced in 1881), were exhibited to show the gilt cover design, the title page—the first to carry the joint imprint of Mathews and Lane—and an inscription written to Lord Alfred Douglas in copy 14 [Taylor] during the second year of their friendship: 'From Oscar to the gilt-mailed Boy. at Oxford in the heart of June.'

Two Junes later (the book appeared on the 11th) Wilde inscribed another book [Hyde] of poetry, THE SPHINX, to the same recipient: 'Bosie, from his friend the author, London '94. Oscar.' This poem had been begun when Wilde was still at Oxford and completed in Paris in 1893. Exhibited with this inscribed copy was the major portion of the manuscript of the work [Hyde] and two copies of the first edition displayed to show the vellum and gilt binding, and the illustration that was parodied by the drawing accompanying Ada Leverson's satire of the book in the 21 July 1894 issue of PUNCH.

Mrs. Leverson, whom Wilde had called 'The Sphinx' from the beginning of their friendship two years before the publication of this book, was the wife of a diamond merchant of considerable

fortune, later a successful novelist herself, and the center of a sa-
lon which included most of the literati of the decade. Responding
to her playful satire, Wilde wrote that 'Punch is delightful and
the drawing a masterpiece of clever caricature. I am afraid she
really was a minx after all. You are the only Sphinx.' Near the
issue of PUNCH, opened to this satire, was shown a book linking
the two authors in a less happy time: the French 1898 edition of
THE BALLAD OF READING GAOL inscribed by Wilde to Mrs. Leverson: 'To the Sphinx of Pleasure: From the Singer of Pain.'

Copies showing the opening stanzas, the title page citing 'C
33'—Wilde's prison identification—as the author, and the un-
derstated binding design, presented the original edition of THE
BALLAD OF READING GAOL. It was begun in late May 1897 at
Berneval and completed in Posilippo in October 1897. Wilde
felt that the 'poem suffers under the difficulty of a divided
aim. . . . Some is realistic, some is romantic: some poetry, some
propaganda. . . . that it is interesting from more points of view
than one is artistically to be regretted. . . . [It is] a poem whose
subject is all wrong, and whose treatment too personal.' It
nevertheless went through six editions—some of 1000 and 1200
copies—within four months and met with appreciative reviews.

The copy [Hyde] in the exhibition opened to the title page
bore Wilde's inscription to Reginald Turner. It was shown with
the contraband letter [Hyde] ('my first and my last') which was
smuggled out of Reading Prison to Turner two days before
Wilde's release. Turner, who was at Oxford with Lord Alfred
Douglas and Max Beerbohm, was the friend whom Wilde
hoped, in this letter, would meet him on his release. Turner
was with Wilde during his last illness and death in Paris on 30
November 1900.

Lord Alfred Douglas intended to dedicate his volume of
POEMS, published by the *Mercure de France* in Paris at the end
of 1896, to Wilde, who was still imprisoned at the time. But
Wilde found the 'proposal . . . grotesque,' and would 'not accept
or allow such a dedication.' The book appeared without one, but
it did include such poems as 'Two Loves' (dedicated to 'The

Sphinx'), which had originally appeared in THE CHAMELEON and with which Wilde had been confronted at his trial. One of the copies of Douglas's book in the exhibition was opened to the final lines of this poem, while another [Hyde] was exhibited to show an inscription, written in Naples in November 1896, to André Gide: 'En témoignage d'admiration et d'affection et en souvenir de Biskrah.' Gide, a year older than Bosie, had seen Wilde several times in Paris before meeting Douglas for the first time during the latter's Algerian trip with Wilde early in 1895. When Wilde left Douglas to return to England for the opening of THE IMPORTANCE OF BEING EARNEST, Gide helped Douglas elope with a caouadji to Biskrah, an oasis that was later to become a locale in Gide's L'Immoraliste.

Near this book was a copy [Hyde] of the second edition of Gide's first book, LES CAHIERS D'ANDRÉ WALTER (Paris, 1891), inscribed to Wilde. The first edition of this autobiographical work, which appeared two months earlier, was almost entirely suppressed by the author on the advice of his friends.

A photograph depicting Douglas in his undergraduate gown at about the time that Lionel Johnson, a close friend, fellow poet and Oxonian, took him to meet Wilde at Wilde's house in Chelsea (probably in January 1891), was shown tipped into a copy [Hyde] of the 1919 collected edition of Douglas's work. Many of the poems in this book were written during the early years of his friendship with Wilde as Douglas's notes written in the margins of this copy document: beside 'Night Coming into a Garden' he wrote, 'Written at Goring in a house Wilde took there just after I left Oxford'; next to the sonnet 'The City of the Soul' he wrote, 'Written in my Villa at Posilippo where Wilde stayed as my guest.' These times and places were further recalled in the exhibition by a photograph of Wilde by Downey dating to the early part of the decade; one of Douglas at age 23, which belonged originally to George Bernard Shaw; and one of Wilde and Douglas together on a holiday on the Continent [all Hyde].

The brief attempt of the Rhymers' Club to revive the literary tavern of Fleet Street and to return to literary discussion as in the days of Samuel Johnson, gathered together a cenacle of poets as diverse as Le Gallienne and Yeats. Yet the two anthologies produced by the club in 1892 and 1894 are a miniature record of the formation of the *fin-de-siècle* style. THE SECOND BOOK OF THE RHYMERS' CLUB was opened to a faded sprig of dried blossoms at Ernest Dowson's 'Extreme Unction,' a poem dedicated in later appearances to Lionel Johnson who once owned both of the copies of the Rhymers' Club volumes shown in the exhibition. Louise Imogen Guiney, into whose possession it later came, noted on the flyleaf of the second volume: 'The flowers on p. 7, over against poor Ernest Dowson's "Extreme Unction," must have been laid there by L. J., the only person to whom this book has formerly belonged.'

The exhibition included letters to John Lane and Elkin Mathews written early in 1894, in which Lionel Johnson records —by his own rejection of 'more than a hundred poems'—the paring of his proposed book to a reasonable length. His publishers apparently had less ambitious plans, for the final book was but half as thick, and many poems less than Johnson's 'absolutely final selection of less than an hundred.' He had similar success in urging Mathews to speed the work of the book's designer, Horne, so that his POEMS might be 'out this side of Christmas.' The book did not appear until 1895. Near two copies of this book—one opened to the title, the other to the text of 'To a Passionist'—was still another letter from Johnson: six pages thanking Louise Imogen Guiney for her book *Patrins*, and recalling 'dear, quaint Wanham, where you expect to meet Julius Ceasar arm-in-arm with George III. Were you there of a Sunday, I wonder, and heard Mass at the little Passionist chapel? It was after Mass there, that I wrote the lines in my book called "To a Passionist." ' Near this, the end papers of Lionel Johnson's copy of H. L. Eads, SHAKER SERMONS: SCRIP-TORATIONAL. CONTAINING THE SUBSTANCE OF SHAKER THEOLOGY, Shakers, New York, 1879, bore, in Johnson's hand, a Latin inscription and a version of his poem 'Ann Lee' initialed and dated, 'L.J. 1896.'

'One of twenty five copies privately printed on Japanese paper for Richard Le Gallienne, Elkin Mathews, John Lane and their friends' of Le Gallienne's ENGLISH POEMS (1892) was exhibited with a contemporary photograph, autographed, of the poet and an extraordinary copy of LIMITED EDITIONS. A PROSE FANCY. TOGETHER WITH CONFESSIO AMANTIS. A SONNET. This copy [Taylor] which originally belonged to Max Beerbohm, was embellished with his drawings: caricatures of Le Gallienne and Wilde, a burlesque of Beardsley's manner, and a rendition of the publisher, John Lane, as a butcher, with carcasses of some of his authors (Lord de Tabley, Beardsley, Le Gallienne, and Wilde) hanging in front of his shop.

Another of the Rhymers, Ernest Dowson, was represented by a copy of his first book of poetry, VERSES, which Smithers published in 1896 with a gold cover design by Beardsley; and by his last book, which became DECORATIONS when the proofs—exhibited alongside the book—of 'Love's Aftermath' were given the author's revisions including the change of title. Accompanying these was Dowson's letter of 5 July 1896, from Pont-Aven in Brittany, in which he responds to proofs of an article concerning him by Arthur Symons which appeared in THE SAVOY in August. 'Would you . . . mind, toning down certain phrases . . . which . . . give . . . too lurid [an] account of me: for have I not been peacefully rusticating these five months en pleine campagne? The sentence "Abroad in the shadier quarters of foreign cities" suggests the too hopelessly disreputable . . . . My wanderings in foreign cities are a result of my chronic restlessness, for indeed I have long since outgrown mine old "curious love of the sordid". . . . If you would suppress a too alcoholic reference [by substituting] "readier means of oblivion" or some such phrase . . . and if you could possibly find a less ignoble word than "very dilapidated," there is nothing in your article which I have any objection to your publishing. . . . I am fortunate in my chronicler.' Before this letter arrived, however, Symons

43

(Yeats later recalled) 'received a wire, "ARRESTED, SELL WATCH AND SEND PROCEEDS." '

Representing other members of the Rhymers' Club were first editions of Ernest Radford's CHAMBERS TWAIN (1890), Ernest Rhys's A LONDON ROSE & OTHER RHYMES (1894), Victor Plarr's IN THE DORIAN MOOD (1896), and the copy of William Butler Yeats's POEMS (1895) with Lionel Johnson's presentation stanzas to Edmund Gosse. The verses, written on the flyleaf, begin:

> Poet and friend, I send
> To you my poet friend:
> Whose perfect poems are
> Star upon star.

Although he was a member of the Rhymers' Club, John Davidson did not contribute to either of its anthologies nor attend its gatherings peacefully. Only a portion of the hundreds of letters in the John Davidson Collection at Princeton could be included in the exhibition. But amongst these were the poet's correspondence with his publishers on the production of his many books, such as FLEET STREET ECLOGUES (1893), BALLADS AND SONGS (1894), FLEET STREET ECLOGUES SECOND SERIES (1896), and THE LAST BALLAD (1899). All of these works were shown in their original editions, as was the ephemeral pamphlet printing of ST. GEORGE'S DAY (New York, 1895). Martin & Sallnow's photograph of the poet, in goatee and mustache, was shown with the manuscript of 'The Yorkshire Morris-Dancers' and the heavily corrected proofs for the 'Midsummer day' section of FLEET STREET ECLOGUES.

John Gray, whom Lionel Johnson referred to as 'a sometimes beautiful oddity,' is associated almost solely with the one book SILVERPOINTS. The exhibition included a complete manuscript, in Gray's hand, of this work (opened to a poem 'Suppressed from the volume on the grounds of indecency'), proofs of the green cloth cover designed by Ricketts, an order blank for the work, and one of the vellum-bound copies. There was also Mathews' agreement with Oscar Wilde to issue Gray's book 'in the autumn on your undertaking the cost of the designs . . . paper, printing and binding of an edition, not exceeding 250 copies.' Accompanying this letter from the Library's collections was a covering letter [Hyde] from Wilde which once enclosed an 'agreement for Mr. Gray's poems.'

On display also was Gray's letter written to Lane on 4 January 1893, listing the proposed recipients (the Princess of Monaco, Harris, Wilde, Swinburne, Dowson, etc.) of publisher's copies of SILVERPOINTS, and mentioning that Frank Harris will review the book for the *Times*: 'I have written to Oscar about copies for me of Silverpoints. Will it be too much if I ask for four large and 12 small?'

Near these materials was a photograph of Gray, signed and dated January 1893 (formerly in the collection of André Raffalovich, who succeeded Wilde as Gray's patron). The poet's striking features recalled the persistent rumor that he was the original of the character of Dorian Gray in Wilde's novel. The identification at one time amused John Gray enough to sign the last page of a letter and poem [Hyde] of January 1891 to Wilde, 'Dorian.' Gray later came to resent the identification and even brought libel action against the *Star*, a London newspaper, for perpetuating it. The case was settled in Gray's favor; had the existence of this letter been known, the case might have been decided differently. The poem which ends the letter is Gray's 'The Honey Child.'

There were manuscripts for Gray's 'Travellers Tales' and 'Sound,' and his letter of 19 January 1895 responding to Mathews' proposal to use the contents of THE BLUE CALENDAR as an 1896 almanac. Gray wished to 'alter or replace the first number. It contains difficulties of expression which would only be called wilful & prejudice success.' Also, a complete set—signed by Gray to A. J. A. Symons—of the four miniature booklets, 'privately printed and not for general distribution,' issued for the Christmases of 1894, 1895, 1896, and 1897 as THE BLUE CALENDAR.

The pamphlet presenting Laurence Binyon's Newdigate prize

45

poem PERSEPHONE (Oxford, 1890) was shown with his LYRIC POEMS (1894), POEMS (1895), FIRST BOOK OF LONDON VISIONS (1896), and SECOND BOOK OF LONDON VISIONS (1899). Michael Field's two books of 1892, STEPHANIA and SIGHT AND SONG, were shown with Lord de Tabley's POEMS DRAMATIC AND LYRICAL (1895) and Arthur Christopher Benson's LE CAHIER JAUNE. POEMS (1892); the latter accompanied by a letter from the author transmitting the book to Curzon. Dollie Radford's SONGS AND OTHER VERSES (Philadelphia, 1895), Stephen Phillips' CHRIST IN HADES (1896), and a copy of W. E. Henley's THE SONG OF THE SWORD (1892) which belonged to Thomas Hardy and bears his pencil notations, were exhibited with the copy of Theodore Wratislaw's ORCHIDS (1896), inscribed with a dedicatory poem, and a copy of his CAPRICES (1893).

Books, manuscripts and letters were shown to represent the work of five poets who, while influenced by, and greatly influential in the Nineties, transcended the definitions and categories usually associated with the decade: Robert Bridges, A. E. Housman, Rudyard Kipling, Francis Thompson, and William Butler Yeats.

Bridges' HUMOURS OF THE COURT (1893) and his privately printed THE GROWTH OF LOVE were exhibited with a manuscript quatrain in Francis Thompson's hand: 'The fairest things have fleetest end;/ Their scent survives their close,/ But the rose's scent has bitterness/ To him that loved the rose'; and with some of that poet's books of the decade: POEMS (1893), SISTER-SONGS (1895), SONGS WING-TO-WING ('Printed for Private Circulation' in 1895), and his VICTORIAN ODE FOR JUBILEE DAY. Kipling's THE SEVEN SEAS (1896) was opened to 'A Song of the English' with stanzas about each of the major cities of the British Empire.

Three copies of the first edition of Housman's A SHROPSHIRE LAD (1896) were shown; one with an inscription 'From the author' also bears a slip from the publishers transmitting the book 'With the Compliments of the Author.' In two letters [Taylor] exhibited beside these books, Housman, on 3 October 1896, asks Professor Beesley to 'accept a copy, which I have told

46

the publishers to send you, of some verses of mine'; and on 17 June 1896 tells his friend Webb that the reviews of the book 'are good, or at any rate, well meaning; only I wish they would not call me a *singer*. One fellow actually says minstrel!'

Yeats, whose POEMS (1895) was exhibited with the materials of the Rhymers' Club, of which he was a member, was further represented with these poets by THE SECRET ROSE (1897), which was opened to show the title page and the frontispiece which reproduces a drawing by John Butler Yeats. Two letters from the latter—the poet's father and the illustrator, as was Kipling's father for his son, of many of his son's books—were shown from the several hundred letters in the Princeton collections. Most of them, like the two exhibited, are elaborately illustrated with ink drawings.

CELTIC REVIVAL

The section of the exhibition presenting the Celtic Revival of the 1890's opened with the letter [Taylor] of early May 1893 in which Wilde thanks George Bernard Shaw 'for Op. 2 of the great Celtic School. . . . I look forward to Op. 4. As for Op. 5, I am lazy, but am rather itching to be at it.' In these cryptic numerical allusions Wilde linked Shaw's and his dramas into a single literary force, for Hesketh Pearson believes that Opus 1 is LADY WINDERMERE'S FAN; 'Op. 2,' WIDOWERS' HOUSES; Opus 3, *A Woman of No Importance*, then running at the Hay-market Theatre; 'Op. 4,' Shaw's next play, *The Philanderer*; and 'Op. 5,' Wilde's subsequent drama, *An Ideal Husband*.

THE COUNTESS KATHLEEN (1892) and THE CELTIC TWILIGHT (1893) recalled the first important publications of the strong and persuasive new voice which attracted artists with Irish affinities. Yeats had founded, in 1891, the National Literary Society, which, seven years later brought into existence the Irish Literary Theatre in Dublin; it was to become the focus of the renaissance in drama of the following decade. Perhaps pre-eminent among the foundations which Yeats himself laid for this movement is THE LAND OF HEART'S DESIRE, which was exhibited in its original manuscript [Taylor] and with playbills from the first performance at the Avenue Theatre, London (April 1894), where it ran for a little over six weeks.

Appropriately at the center of the Celtic materials was a photograph of the entrance to Coole, Lady Gregory's residence near Gort in Ireland—an inviting lane tunnelling into the distance through stands of ancient trees—and a drawing of her visitors' book there: the initialed tree, bearing the carved initials of visitors like the Yeatses, Shaw, O'Casey, and 'A.E.' It was Lady Gregory's hospitality, patronage and intelligent interest, which fostered friendship among the Celtic writers, gave birth to the Irish National Theatre, and also provided the security and solitude for the writing of some of Yeats's finest poetry.

For this group around Lady Gregory, the Irish renaissance began in 1893 with Yeats's THE CELTIC TWILIGHT and Douglas Hyde's *Love Songs of Connacht*. Anglo-Irish like Lady Gregory, Douglas Hyde became a 'vernacular poet of the first order, whose songs passed into folk culture in his lifetime.' Included in the exhibition was his earlier work, BESIDE THE FIRE (1890), a collection of traditional poems and tales which appeared with literal prose translations intended as a sort of crib to help the student of Irish. Representing his scholarly activity was ʒıoꞁꞁᴀ ᴀn ꝥıuʒᴀ OR, THE LAD OF THE FERULE, which Hyde edited and translated as Volume One in a series issued by the Irish Text Society of which he was president.

The November 1896 SAVOY, opened to the final page of 'Morag of the Glen,' introduced the most important literary figure of the Celtic Revival in Scotland—'Fiona Macleod,' whom we now recognize as the novelist and critic William Sharp. Of special interest were the letters exhibited in which William Sharp talks of a new book issued under his pseudonym as that by 'my cousin and dear friend, Miss Fiona Macleod.'

Grant Allen's article in THE FORTNIGHTLY REVIEW of 1 February 1891, in which he recognized the phenomenon of a 'Celtic movement' in English art, was exhibited near a group of the contemporary works of this movement: IDEALS IN IRELAND, edited by Lady Gregory and written by A.E., D. P. Moran, George Moore, Douglas Hyde, Standish O'Grady, and W. B. Yeats (1891); TWO ESSAYS ON THE REMNANT which W. K. Magee wrote under the pseudonym of John Eglinton and issued in Dublin in 1894; Stephen Gwynn's copy of A.E.'s THE EARTH BREATH AND OTHER POEMS (1897); LITERARY IDEALS IN IRELAND by John Eglinton, W. B. Yeats, A.E., and W. Larminie (1899); and the first annual volume of BELTAINE, the organ of the Irish Literary Theatre, edited by W. B. Yeats, the first issue of which appeared in May 1899.

CRITICISM

Since Wilde's accomplishment as a critic may come to transcend most other aspects of his art, it was fortunate that the exhibition could present the manuscript, in Wilde's hand, of 'The True Function of Criticism' [Hyde]. First printed in the July and September 1890 issues of THE NINETEENTH CENTURY and later, with the new title, 'The Critic as Artist,' in INTENTIONS (1891), the ending was an afterthought. In the copy [Hyde] of INTENTIONS exhibited is tipped in a manuscript ending to this essay which was sent to the publisher of the journal where it first appeared: 'Kindly add to the end of my article the following . . .' writes Wilde, adding the final sentences.

However much the criticism of the period concentrated on art, society was not ignored. Oscar Wilde bridged the chasm between the individualism of the Decadents and the communal aspirations of the more advanced social revolutionaries. His essay 'The Soul of Man Under Socialism' first appeared under the editorship of Frank Harris in THE FORTNIGHTLY REVIEW [Hyde] for February 1891 alongside Grant Allen's 'The Celt in English Art.' Allen wrote Wilde: 'Will you allow me to thank you most heartily for your noble and beautiful essay in this month's *Fortnightly*? I would have written every line of it myself—if only I had known how.' Representing its wide distribution before it appeared in book form in May 1895 were two printings of March 1891 and January 1892 issued by the Humboldt Publishing Company of New York in its LIBRARY OF SCIENCE.

A volume of the FABIAN ESSAYS IN SOCIALISM recalled George Bernard Shaw's activities in this same tradition. As editor of this influential series of tracts—he wrote a number of them himself— he was a tireless and effective propagandist of the collectivism upheld by the Fabian Society. It was in such revolutionary circles that George Bernard Shaw's name was most meaningful at the beginning of the decade. The less distinguished political criticism of the decade was illustrated by THE WHIRLWIND, A LIVELY AND ECCENTRIC NEWSPAPER, THE ORGAN OF THE HON. STUART ERSKINE AND MR. HERBERT VIVIAN [Hyde]. The lithographs by Whistler, interspersed between its sheets of news, give this periodical its chief interest today.

PERIODICALS

'No other decade in English history has produced so many distinctive and ambitious publications,' wrote Holbrook Jackson of the periodicals of the Nineties. The most famous of them is THE YELLOW BOOK, a 'hard cover magazine' published in London from 1894 to 1897 by John Lane of The Bodley Head (and in an American edition by Copeland & Day in Boston). The American-born Henry Harland was literary editor and Aubrey Beardsley art editor for the first year and a half of its existence. For both admirers and detractors of the new trends, THE YELLOW BOOK epitomized the time. The exhibition presented this influential periodical in a complete run of the volumes produced under Beardsley's designs, accompanied by the small paper-covered booklets announcing each of these first five volumes. The prospectus for Volume One bears Beardsley's original design for the first cover of THE YELLOW BOOK, a design replaced by another of his when the book appeared; the announcement for Volume Five bears the controversial cover design which led to its suppression and the artist's dismissal. These ephemeral prospectuses were overshadowed, however, by the unique copy of

Volume Five in the cover Beardsley designed. This 'dummy' volume was the only one produced with the Beardsley cover before a design by W. H. Townsend was substituted because Wilfred Meynell and William Watson had threatened to withdraw their contributions to the magazine and their books from Lane's publishing house unless Beardsley's drawings were eliminated from Volume Five and future issues. This incident—recalled in the exhibition by two cablegrams sent by Watson to John Lane, then travelling in the United States—resulted in Beardsley's dismissal as art editor and was a reflection of the suspicion engendered at the time by the Wilde trials.

A letter of 31 August 1894 from Henry Harland to Lionel Johnson regretting that he could not use a play that had been submitted by a friend of Johnson's 'in the Y.B.; it is so painful. Everybody sends me tearful contributions, and I want gay ones,' suggested that editor's point of view. While Volume Ten—accompanied by Laurence Housman's ink drawing (Pre-Raphaelite in feeling rather than modern) which was reproduced in it—suggested the graphic changes which the magazine underwent. Yet even THE YELLOW BOOK could not avoid Beardsley completely. In the exhibition was the large poster used to advertise Volume Eleven in October 1896 which incorporates one of Beardsley's earlier designs.

After Beardsley's withdrawal from THE YELLOW BOOK, it was the publisher, Leonard Smithers, who recognized the importance of giving this illustrator complete control of the format of a similarly ambitious publication. Standing firmly for the ideas and art of the Decadence at its darkest hour, Smithers gave birth to THE SAVOY, with Beardsley as art editor and Arthur Symons as literary editor, and thus produced 'the most satisfying achievement of *fin-de-siècle* journalism.' Exhibited with a complete set of this magazine in its original pink and blue wrappers were: the handsome prospectus for the venture; the October 1896 broadside announcement that ' "The Savoy" will be discontinued after the issue of No. 8, in December next'; a letter from Beardsley to Smithers concerning the designs for the final issue;

a second set of the journal 'bound in 3 volumes in artistic cloth cases, with an original cover design by Mr. Aubrey Beardsley'; and the green and red poster employing the cover design of the last issue to announce this run 'Complete in three volumes.'

Subsidiary to these lavish productions was a proliferation of publications of less ambitious, but equally elevated, policy. Many of these magazines were born and nurtured by undergraduates at Oxford and Cambridge. Beardsley designed covers for THE CAMBRIDGE A.B.C., and Wilde contributed to THE SPIRIT LAMP before and after it came under Lord Alfred Douglas's editorship during his last year at Oxford. Max Beerbohm's caricatures embellished another Oxford magazine, THE OCTOPUS. Complete runs of these scarce periodicals in their original form were in the exhibition.

John Francis Bloxam, who as an Oxford undergraduate produced the first (and only) issue of THE CHAMELEON, asked Lord Alfred Douglas for a contribution and hoped Wilde might be persuaded to write for it also. Wilde offered his 'Phrases and Philosophies for the Use of the Young,' which he had originally intended as successors to those already published in THE SATURDAY REVIEW, and Douglas contributed two poems. One of the latter, 'Two Loves,' and the anonymous story, 'The Priest and the Acolyte,' which was attributed to Wilde but was actually written by the magazine's editor, were used as evidence against Wilde in his trials. Shown in the exhibition with the original issue of THE CHAMELEON were contemporary separate printings of both THE PRIEST AND THE ACOLYTE and PHRASES AND PHILOSOPHIES FOR THE USE OF THE YOUNG.

While many of these journals were ultimately dependent upon the enthusiasms and energies of one person, William Sharp's THE PAGAN REVIEW was completely an individual production. Its single issue, which he designed and produced, in August 1892, included contributions written entirely by himself under various pseudonyms to promote the 'new paganism.' The deception was carried even to advertisements for non-existent works by non-existent contributors, such as those for Gascoigne and W. S. Fanshawe mentioned on the pages opened in the exhibition.

Issues selected from the runs of THE DOME, THE NEW REVIEW, THE HOBBY HORSE, THE QUARTO, PICK-ME-UP, THE STUDIO and THE BUTTERFLY were further evidence of the quality of the periodicals of the decade. Even the more popular magazines of the period came to give serious consideration to visual as well as literary art. Accompanying each issue of THE ALBEMARLE was an original lithograph. Many of them, such as the two displayed in the exhibition with a calling card bearing his butterfly signature, were by hands as masterful as those of James Abbott McNeill Whistler. Whistler's anticipation of much in Wilde and his era precipitated numerous aesthetic and legal battles. His THE GENTLE ART OF MAKING ENEMIES AS PLEASINGLY EXEMPLIFIED IN MANY INSTANCES, WHEREIN THE SERIOUS ONES OF THIS EARTH, CAREFULLY EXASPERATED, HAVE BEEN PRETTILY SPURRED ON TO UNSEEMLINESS AND INDISCRETION, WHILE OVERCOME BY AN UNDUE SENSE OF RIGHT (1895), which chronicles some of the more celebrated of his legal and aesthetic forays, was represented in the exhibition by the copy (opened to one of the many exchanges between Wilde and Whistler) inscribed to the painter's solicitor, William Webb.

SCIENCE FICTION AND THE SUPERNATURAL

Wilde's place in the development of science fiction and the supernatural was represented by THE PICTURE OF DORIAN GRAY. The original publication of the novel, in the July 1890 number of LIPPINCOTT'S MONTHLY MAGAZINE, precipitated such extensive criticism on moral grounds that Wilde wrote a number of rejoinders. Included in the exhibition was a letter [Hyde] to Arthur Fish, in which Wilde wrote, 'I am delighted you like Dorian Gray—it has been attacked on ridiculous grounds, but I think will be ultimately recognised as a real work of art with a strong ethical lesson inherent in it.' The novel was published in book form in April 1891, though the large-paper edition of 250 signed copies did not appear until the first of July. Copy

Number 1 of the latter, with the prospectus of this limited issue, was exhibited with copies of the first edition inscribed to Clyde Fitch; to Lionel Johnson (who, sometime after Wilde's fall in 1895, added his own note in Latin which reads, in translation: 'The Lord have mercy on my friend, the writer!'); to Wilde's wife, Constance; and the copy which belonged years later to Lord Alfred Douglas's wife whose name, Olive, is written at the top of the title page [all Hyde].

Du Maurier's creative energies, which were earlier devoted to black-and-white illustration (his satires in PUNCH and his illustrations for the fiction of the period were considered pre-eminent), were turned to the novel only at the end of his life. His second novel, TRILBY, was an extraordinary success—its popularity, in fact, so affected every level of English society that Henry James refers to its influence, in a letter included in the exhibition, as 'the strange Trilby madness.' It is a psychological thriller set in the Bohemia of Paris where du Maurier's stormy friendship with Whistler began in 1857. Issued originally in HARPER'S NEW MONTHLY MAGAZINE, TRILBY included a characterization and illustrations so unmistakably satirizing Whistler, that the latter's protests to the publisher were heeded; in the first edition of the book both the illustrations and the text referring to Joe Sibley (Whistler) were suppressed. The most famous of these suppressed illustrations, 'The Two Apprentices,' was exhibited with a first edition of the book (1895). Du Maurier died in the year following the publication of TRILBY of the same disease that carried off its villain, Svengali. The little keepsake portfolio, A SOUVENIR OF 'TRILBY' BY PAUL M. POTTER (FOUNDED ON GEORGE DU MAURIER'S NOVEL.) PRODUCED FOR THE FIRST TIME IN LONDON AT THE THEATRE ROYAL, HAYMARKET, ON THE 30TH OCTOBER, 1895, BY HERBERT BEERBOHM TREE, and two of the photoengravings it included—one showing Mr. Tree as Svengali, the other Miss Dorothea Baird as Trilby—suggested but one of the popular forms this story assumed. Another drama of the supernatural playing contemporaneously was *Dr. Jekyll and Mr. Hyde*—recalled in the exhibition by the playbill of the

Lyceum performance with Richard Mansfield, and a photograph, twice exposed, showing him simultaneously as Jekyll and Hyde.

Both of the H. G. Wells volumes that were shown are presentation copies: Wells's first novel, THE INVISIBLE MAN (1895) [Taylor], is inscribed to the author's brother, Frank; THE TIME MACHINE (1895) [Taylor], to Major Sawford. Arthur Conan Doyle's THE MEMOIRS OF SHERLOCK HOLMES (1894) was shown with Arthur Machen's THE GREAT GOD PAN which appeared the same year. In the latter and in collections of his prose from this decade, such as THE HOUSE OF SOULS (1906), which was also exhibited, Machen took romance into the abodes of terror in a manner as startling as it was elementally right. But among the more enduring products of this genre was Henry James's 'The Turn of the Screw,' which was represented in the exhibition by its original appearance in book form with another tale, 'Covering End,' under the single title, THE TWO MAGICS (1898).

NATURALISM AND THE NOVEL

In his 'The Decay of Lying: A Dialogue,' which was exhibited as it originally appeared in the January 1889 issue of THE NINETEENTH CENTURY, Wilde upheld the emerging naturalism of the current fiction. His argument took more permanent form in his book of essays, INTENTIONS (1891), and continued to influence the art of the period. The realist movement spread among writers of fiction even more rapidly than it invaded the drama. But despite the preparation which the cheap editions of Zola had afforded the English public, when Thomas Hardy issued JUDE THE OBSCURE and George Moore, ESTHER WATERS, there was vigorous protest. The ineffectual suppressions of these works in a few lending libraries drew the special attention to them which they deserved.

Beneath Rothenstein's portrait of Hardy in ENGLISH PORTRAITS (1898), was the copy of JUDE THE OBSCURE in which Hardy dated his inscription to Charles Whibley 'December 1895,' though the title page bears 1896 as the year of publication. The October 1896 issue of THE SAVOY was opened to the

5 5

article by Havelock Ellis defending the naturalism of JUDE THE OBSCURE. Next to it Lionel Johnson's THE ART OF THOMAS HARDY (1894) bore an inscription by the author to Edmund Gosse:

> To whom, if not to you, Sir, should I send
> My book about your friend?
> You with approving kindliness will take
> Its praises, for his sake:
> As to its censure, who's the censor? Why
> I am: and who am I?

Tipped in was a note from Hardy ending, 'It is always the dirtiest-minded who clamour for "clean" literature; they can read harm into the most harmless book. Remember what Swift says about them.'

Placed with a copy of TESS OF THE D'URBERVILLES (1891)— which marked one of Hardy's steps toward the naturalism that culminated in JUDE THE OBSCURE—was a letter [Taylor] to the publisher William Heinemann in which Hardy reveals that he had 'taken steps to get all my novels into one list' and to issue 'a uniform edition of these books.'

The storm produced by the reception of JUDE THE OBSCURE and ESTHER WATERS was heightened by the appearance in 1895 of Grant Allen's THE WOMAN WHO DID. A copy of the first edition of this book by an author who also wrote works on evolution and kindred topics was opened to the declaration: 'Written at Perugia spring 1893 for the first time in my life wholly and solely to satisfy my own taste and my own conscience.' Another acknowledged disciple of the realistic school of fiction was Hubert Crackanthorpe. With his 1894 collection of short stories, WREAKAGE, was shown a letter in which he proposes to John Lane a scheme 'to unite in a single volume a number of short stories, written by *young* men, all genuine artists of distinction: in fact, a book, which would, in a limited sense, resemble the Rhymers' Club volume. Two names occur to me at once, Lionel Johnson and Ernest Dowson: then, these others: Yeats, Frank Harris (?), Wedmore, and Henry Harland. . . .'

The realistic school influenced the birth of occasional novels from writers who were not exclusively realists, but who were impelled by the mood of the moment to produce works which joined in its most extreme tendency. The exhibition included as an example of these works W. Somerset Maugham's LIZA OF LAMBETH (1897). Henry James's WHAT MAISIE KNEW (1898) and Robert Louis Stevenson's WEIR OF HERMISTON (1896) represented still other directions which the novel took in this decade.

THE SENSE OF EMPIRE

The sense of Empire, intensified by the celebration of Queen Victoria's Diamond Jubilee of 1897, was represented in the exhibition by examples of works published in the Nineties by Joseph Conrad, Rider Haggard, and Rudyard Kipling. First editions of Conrad's ALMAYER'S FOLLY (1895) and his AN OUTCAST OF THE ISLANDS (1896) were exhibited with THE NIGGER OF THE 'NARCISSUS' (1898). The latter was accompanied by one of the examples—printed privately for Conrad in November of 1902 in an issue of 100 copies—of the novel's suppressed 1898 preface; this one inscribed: 'To Richard Curle. This suppressed preface was printed by W. S. Henley in the New Review at the end of the novel as the author's afterword. Joseph Conrad.'

Beneath a letter from Oscar Wilde inviting Rider Haggard to meet Lady Ardilaun, 'a woman of great charm and appreciation,' appeared the novelist's MONTEZUMA'S DAUGHTER (1893), HEART OF THE WORLD (1896), and THE PEOPLE OF THE MIST (1894). The romance of 1894 was opened to a wood engraving of the Outram brothers, whose father, through bankruptcy and suicide, has left them penniless, swearing in the hall of the family estate, which has just been sold at auction, never to return to England until they have found a fortune in 'the land of the Children of the Mist' (Africa) and can return with the means 'to retrieve the past.'

The two volumes of Kipling's JUNGLE BOOKS of 1894 and 1895 were shown with covers in superb condition displaying, against a dark blue ground, the brilliant gilt designs of the author's father, John Lockwood Kipling, who had many affinities with the Pre-Raphaelites and illustrated many of his son's works.

Near the materials representing the sense of Empire were exhibited pages from a manuscript draft of Rudyard Kipling's novel *The Light That Failed*, which appeared in the January 1891 number of LIPPINCOTT'S MAGAZINE. This periodical, which was issued in both an English and an American edition, had published during 1890 Conan Doyle's *The Sign of Four* and Oscar Wilde's THE PICTURE OF DORIAN GRAY.

Kipling's novel, which has a painter as its principal character, had much to say of art and artists. In the chapter that was exhibited, Dick Heldar, fresh from the colorful sights of the Mediterranean world, expresses his exasperation with London aesthetic circles. The Londoners (reads the manuscript) 'who haven't even been to Algiers tell you first that it's borrowed from Holman Hunt and then that it isn't Art.' In the printed version the reference to Holman Hunt has been deleted. Kipling elsewhere expressed himself on the subject of the aesthetes. Recently returned from India to London, he wrote in 'In Partibus':

> But I consort with long-haired things
> In velvet collar-rolls
> Who talk about the Aims of Art
> And 'theories' and 'goals',
> And moo, and coo with womenfolk
> About their blessed souls.

Wilde's opinions on Kipling were expressed in his dialogue-essay, 'The True Function and Value of Criticism,' first published in the July and September 1890 issues of THE NINETEENTH CENTURY. In the passage exhibited from this essay, Wilde writes that 'From the point of view of literature Mr. Kipling is a man of talent who drops his aspirates. From the point of view of life he is a reporter who knows vulgarity better than anyone has ever known it. Dickens knew its clothes. Mr. Kipling knows its essence. He is our best authority on the second-rate. He terrifies us by his truth, and makes his sordid subject-matter marvellous by the brilliancy of its setting.' When Wilde's essay reappeared in his 1891 INTENTIONS (the copy [Hyde] exhibited was inscribed to Clyde Fitch), the passage had been changed to end: 'He is our first authority on the second rate, and has seen marvellous things through key-holes, and his backgrounds are real works of art.'

REACTION AND RIDICULE

Two pen and watercolor caricatures by Beerbohm—one of Oscar Wilde and John Toole at the Garrick Club in 1893 and the other of Wilde and Will Rothenstein—visually set the tone of the case representing the reaction to, and ridicule of Wilde and the aesthetic influences associated with him. The most renowned satire of the period, Robert Hichens' THE GREEN CARNATION (1894), focused its mordant humor specifically on Wilde. But the exhibition's inclusion, along with Hichens' book, of Max Beerbohm's THE HAPPY HYPOCRITE and David Hodge's THE QUEST OF THE GILT-EDGED GIRL BY RICHARD DE LYRIENNE (satirizing Le Gallienne's *The Quest of the Golden Girl*), issued in 1897 as numbers one and two in a series called the 'Bodley Booklets,' suggested that few authors of the period were invulnerable to ridicule. An issue of THE GRANTA, an undergraduate production at Cambridge, was exhibited opened to a prospectus for *The Yellow Boot*; it was illustrated with a parody of Beardsley's design for the cover of the original prospectus for THE YELLOW BOOK, and promised articles by such authors as 'Richard Le Guinneahenne,' 'Flaubert Crockonwheales,' and 'Melia Mascula Dowdie.'

One of the more specific of the satires, and certainly among the most scarce, is THE POET AND THE PUPPETS, A TRAVESTIE SUGGESTED BY 'LADY WINDERMERE'S FAN.' BY CHARLES BROOKFIELD. MUSIC BY J. M. GLOVER. The copy [Hyde] of this book was accompanied in the exhibition not only by a letter [Hyde] from Glover in which he writes of Brookfield's and his 'little "slap" at Mr. O'Flaherty Wilde which is in rehearsal . . . ,' but also by the sheet music for Glover's NEVER RECOGNISE YOUR MA-IN-

LAW AT ALL . . . SUNG WITH THE GREATEST SUCCESS BY MR. ERIC LEWIS IN THE TRAVESTY ON "LADY WINDERMERE'S FAN."

All the forces of opposition to Wilde and his art met in the public response to Wilde's trials and imprisonment. One of the documents surviving from this period of Wilde's career, and included in the exhibition, is the rapidly scrawled note [Hyde] to Lord Alfred Douglas which was written at the moment of Wilde's arrest on 5 April 1895. 'I will be at Bow Street Police Station tonight—no bail possible I am told. Would you ask Percy, and George Alexander, and Waller, at the Haymarket, to attend to give bail. Would you also wire Humphreys to appear at Bow Street for me. . . . Also, come to see me.' The following day Wilde was charged, refused bail, and imprisoned at Holloway until his trial began on 26 April. The jury disagreed and a new trial was ordered. On 25 May Wilde was found guilty and sentenced to two years' imprisonment at hard labor. The following August, at Sorrento, Douglas wrote an article in defense of Wilde. It was intended for the *Mercure de France*, but when Wilde learned that it included some of his letters to Douglas from prison, he prevented its appearance. Since Douglas later destroyed 150 of Wilde's letters to him, including all of those from Holloway, the manuscript of this unpublished article, presented in the exhibition, is one of the few sources that survives to suggest the character of this correspondence.

THE GREAT WEST-END SCANDAL [Hyde] and THE LIFE OF OSCAR WILDE AS PROSECUTOR AND PRISONER [Hyde], both penny pamphlets, reflected one pole of the public reaction to the revelations of Wilde's trials. Balancing this—in the era of Krafft-Ebing and Havelock Ellis, and the beginnings of serious psychological inquiry written for an intelligent public—were a few sober inquiries such as that included in the exhibition by the playwright and patron of John Gray, André Raffalovich. His 'L'Affaire Oscar Wilde' in the 1896 volume, URANISME ET UNISEXUALITÉ, is part of a series of scientific works edited by the criminologist Lacassagne.

The concern for visual form which pervaded every aspect of printing during the decade was so exceptional in its effect that no portion of the exhibition escaped the presentation of materials of interest from the standpoint of graphic art. That grouping which focused specifically on book design and its allied arts, was properly dominated by Aubrey Beardsley, the leader and most characteristic illustrator of the aesthetic renaissance of the 1890's.

The commission which established Beardsley's reputation and which he executed when he was but 20 years of age, was the edition of LE MORTE D'ARTHUR which John M. Dent published in 1893 to rival the work of William Morris's Kelmscott Press. This landmark in the history of fine printing was represented in the exhibition by volumes of the first edition, printed on Dutch paper, in both the cloth and vellum bindings; by the book as issued in parts, with wrappers bearing the artist's bold drawings; three of Beardsley's original drawings for chapter headings; and openings to characteristic illustrations.

Almost simultaneously with the production of LE MORTE D'ARTHUR, Beardsley illustrated Oscar Wilde's SALOME. 'That tragic daughter of passion appeared on Thursday last, and is now dancing for the head of the English public,' wrote Wilde to a friend in late February of 1893. Exhibited with Beardsley's English edition—dedicated 'To my friend Lord Alfred Bruce Douglas, the translator of my play'—was the first printing of the original French text [Hyde], in what Wilde called its 'Tyrian purple and tired silver' wrappers, which followed the appearance of Douglas's translation by only thirteen days.

Not only was the production of the play, which Sarah Bernhardt had begun rehearsing, banned by the Lord Chamberlain, but at least three of Beardsley's original illustrations were also suppressed. One of these suppressed plates was exhibited, as was still another copy of the complete book, in an extravagant Rivière binding [Hyde] which reproduced in leather inside the front and back covers, two of Beardsley's illustrations, including that for the frontispiece with the portrait of Wilde rising as a moon on the horizon.

Beardsley's letter to John Lane commenting on a proof for the cover of Ernest Dowson's THE PIERROT OF THE MINUTE (1896)—a scholar has said it 'seems to sum up and crown the achievement of the great period of his art'—was exhibited near one of these proofs. There were as well a copy of the book showing this same design impressed in gilt on the vellum cover, the prospectus for the work ('Mr. Beardsley has designed a Frontispiece, Vignette, Cul-de-Lampe, Initial Letter, and Binding Design, for this volume, which are amongst the most charming Drawings which have come from his pen'), and another copy opened to the tailpiece.

In the same year that he designed Dowson's book, he was at work on the Keynote Series, a multi-volume set issued by John Lane which reprinted contemporary novels and short stories. The 'General Notice of the Series,' announcing books whose covers were to bear 'Twenty-one designs by Aubrey Beardsley,' was exhibited with five typical volumes: Victoria Crosse's THE WOMAN WHO DIDN'T, Grant Allen's THE WOMAN WHO DID, Arthur Machen's THE GREAT GOD PAN AND THE INMOST LIGHT, Fiona Macleod's THE MOUNTAIN LOVERS, and M. P. Shiel's PRINCE ZALESKI.

Two of Beardsley's large posters—one, without letters, depicting a woman reading in a winged-back chair; the other advertising the Pseudonym and Autonym Library—and two book bindings which he designed in 1897 for Vincent O'Sullivan's THE HOUSES OF SIN (shown with the manuscript, in O'Sullivan's hand, of his 'Ballads of the Dust') and Ben Jonson's VOLPONE, were shown with the dedication copy of the artist's 1898 edition of Pope's THE RAPE OF THE LOCK. Attached to the page dedicating this book 'To Edmund Gosse' is the note in which Beardsley urged Gosse to 'accept it as a friend rather than a critic. . . .' It was shortly after completing this design that Beardsley began considering work for the projected periodical *The Peacock*, which Smithers planned to take the place of THE SAVOY. One of the artist's conditions to an acceptance of Smithers' offer to be its art editor was that it be 'quite agreed that Oscar Wilde contributes nothing to the magazine, anonymously, pseudonymously or otherwise.' But Beardsley was dead in March 1898, of tuberculosis, at twenty-six. Three portraits of him were included in the exhibition: an unattributed full-length profile in garish colors, an acid caricature in pencil and crayon by Max Beerbohm, and a lithograph by Will Rothenstein. The latter, with the same artist's portrait of George Bernard Shaw (both in Rothenstein's ENGLISH PORTRAITS [1898]) was shown with an original sketch book and the GUTTER-SNIPES (1899) of Phil May, thus juxtaposing two poles of the black-and-white art that distinguished the Nineties.

Responding to the first public notice of his A HOUSE OF POMEGRANATES, Wilde wrote: 'The writer of the paragraph in question states that the decorative designs that make lovely my book A HOUSE OF POMEGRANATES, are by the hand of Mr. Shannon, while the delicate dreams that separate and herald each story are by Mr. Ricketts. The contrary is the case. Mr. Shannon is the drawer of dreams, and Mr. Ricketts is the subtle and fantastic decorator. Indeed it is to Mr. Ricketts that the entire decorative design of the book is due. . . .' Facing Charles Ricketts' design in one of the copies exhibited [Hyde] are the original drawings for each of his 'decorations.' A second copy [Hyde] of the book, once given to the English actress, Constance Collier, was opened to show on the reverse of the page dedicating the volume to the author's wife, a caricature by Max Beerbohm of Wilde.

Charles Ricketts' work was exemplified not only in A HOUSE OF POMEGRANATES but also in THE SPHINX. A copy of this book by Wilde was opened in the exhibition to Ricketts' flowing linear illustrations in which he explored, as had Beardsley, the 'art nouveau.' This style reacted against, rather than followed, the decade's most significant revolution in the design of books: that begun by William Morris's establishment of the Kelmscott Press in 1891. THE WOOD BEYOND THE WORLD, which Morris not only wrote but which also was 'printed by him at the Kelmscott Press, Upper Mall, Hammersmith, finished the 30th day of May, 1891'; the LAUDE BEATAE MARIAE VIRGINIS (Kelmscott, 1896) and uncut sheets of THE STORY OF GUNNLAUG THE WORM-TONGUE AND RAVEN THE SKALD (Chiswick Press, 1891) were exhibited to exemplify the quality of design and craftsmanship which was the objective of Morris and his followers.

They were closely associated with the Pre-Raphaelites, eclectic in their approach, eager to employ their conception of fifteenth-century typography, and characteristically they imprisoned each page in intricate border designs and ornament. It was in rejection of this group that the book considered the culmination of craftsmanship and thinking in the graphic arts of the Nineties was produced. In the DOVES BIBLE, printed in the early years of the twentieth century at the Doves Press, which had been founded at the end of the decade by T. J. Cobden-Sanderson and Emery Walker, the objective was one of 'the simple arrangement of the whole Book . . . rather than by the addition and splendour of applied ornament.' The achievement was shown in two volumes opened to the initial sentences of 'The Song of Solomon' and 'The Book of the Prophet Isaiah.'

The art particularly associated with the design of bindings was represented in Ricketts' gilt arabesque lily-of-the-valley on the vellum cover of John Addington Symonds' IN THE KEY OF BLUE (1893); by the 1899 edition of Yeats's POEMS, with a design of swirling gilt leaves on a dark-blue cloth ground; by the serpentine gilt lines on the cloth binding of Kipling's THE SEVEN SEAS (New York, 1897); and by the thicket-silhouette on the cover of Maurice Hewlett's THE FOREST LOVERS (1898). The more elaborate productions of hand binders of the period were exemplified in a decidedly art-nouveau binding (a delicately interlaced design with floral inlays on a ground of pointillé) by the Hempstead bindery on a copy of Samuel Rogers' ITALY.

The pervasive belief that the physical form of books should be as carefully wrought as their literary content gave brilliance to every aspect of the exhibition. Playbills, posters, drawings, and caricatures added visual distinction throughout the gallery. With the wealth and variety of materials available the problem of selection was often difficult, but it is hoped that the exhibition fully suggested the fascination of the Nineties.